I Took the Long Way Home

By Jessica G. Parenti

Dedication Page

To Lee
For demonstrating the true meaning of Christianity
Even in death, you claimed the victory

To Mom and Dad
For your faithfulness to the Lord and your prayers

To my son, Anthony
For the joy you bring to my life

To my brother, Antonio
For the great man of God into which you will rise

To my dear cousin, Paul
Life will just never be the same without you

Contents

Author's Forward

This book is about a girl named Stephanie Cavelli.

Stephanie is thirty years old. She is a pastor's daughter. She is also the mother of a fourteen-year-old son. Stephanie was born and raised in a wonderful Christian home, with parents who genuinely loved and served Christ.

As I write this forward, I am twenty-nine-years old, a pastor's daughter and the mother of a wonderful young man named Anthony, who is thirteen years old. I too was born to and raised by parents who genuinely loved Christ and put Him first in everything.

This is the story of a girl who traded her priceless upbringing, her salvation, for the illusions of this world, a girl who searched the world for peace and love, only to find that the Love for which she yearned had been available all along—in the one place she refused to look.

As you read Stephanie's story, you will find mine between and betwixt the pages of hers. Many of Stephanie's experiences mirror my own, while some are the product of fiction.

I will take you through the character's journey back to the Cross. We will begin in present day, then travel way back into the past and then arrive in the present again. When we finally make it back home, you will discover a unique testimony of grace.

This is the story of girl who took the long way home.

May you find the great Love and Friend that I have.

Those who forget God have no hope. They are like rushes without any mire to grow in; or grass without water to keep it alive. . . A man without God is trusting in a spider's web. Everything he counts on will collapse.

Job 8:11-14 (The Living Bible)

1 New Year's Revelation

It's New Year's Eve, two minutes to a brand-new year. I'm standing among a small crowd of thirty- and forty-something socialites on the rooftop deck of a magnificent penthouse condominium in Center City Philadelphia. I stand here in wait for the much-anticipated fireworks extravaganza that is set to ignite momentarily along the city's historic Penn's Landing.

The night sky is clear, with few stars ablaze through the blackness. It's cold but not unbearable. The warm bodies around me feel like an electric blanket, negating the insufficient winter outerwear I chose for the evening: a thin, black leather jacket—which I had to wear because it matched perfectly with my new stiletto boots.

Like those around me, I'm welcoming the new year with overpriced champagne, gourmet Italian food, and a half-hearted resolution to exercise regularly and earn more money. Apart from a few minor distinctions, each person in attendance is the same. They have everything anyone could want: beauty, success, wealth, designer clothes, and stunning significant others. Yet there's something missing, something about their smiles that seems disingenuous. I scan the crowd, trying to identify what it is in these seemingly complete people that just doesn't seem right. At this point, I can't quite put my finger on it.

The owner of the condo, Damian, a hotshot entertainment lawyer, the best and most sought-after in the city, climbs on a table to make a toast. Cuban cigar in one hand and cut-crystal champagne flute in the other, his legs wobble and his arms lunge for those around him as he struggles to stand erect. Ripples of Dom Pérignon slap against the rounded sides of his glass as he finally gains his balance and stands to his feet.

A handsome Hispanic man, in his early-forties, with bronzed skin and sparse, wavy hair behind a receding hairline, he clears his throat loudly enough to rouse the crowd's attention for a toast. I'm eager to hear what he has to say. I expect something meaningless and shallow like the other New Year's Eve toasts I've heard over the years.

"As we peek through the archway of the new year that stands before us," Damian begins, "raise your glasses with me." He speaks eloquently but with an undertone that leaks an unmistakable hint of sarcasm.

"To the new year," a few noble listeners yell.

"May you all become as rich as I am," Damian declares with a sneaky grin, pausing while numerous glassy eyes wander toward him in unconscious apprehension, "so next year someone else can pay for this party for a change." A cheer of satisfaction and laughter fills the air as Damian lifts his glass as if it's his own personal trophy. It seems he knows just how to please this crowd. "Happy wealthy New Year," he says as the crowd responds in unison. *Happy wealthy New Year.*

Each person, myself included, raises his or her glass in celebration. And, just as our glasses clang, the sky crackles above us followed by a burst of brilliant colors, sprinkling streaks of light across the black sky as an orchestrated display of fireworks precedes the dawning of yet another year.

A roar of voices floats up from the streets below us, where a sea of cars impedes the normal flow of traffic. People are sitting on the hoods of their cars, drinking beer from green bottles, tooting cheap horns and tossing confetti—all gathered to watch the show of exploding lights. "Ten," the crowd bellows. "Nine." Our small group assembles by the edge of the deck, looking down at those unable to afford balcony seating. "Eight," we all join in. "Seven, six, five, four, three, two…"

"One!" we exclaim.

Car horns blast as a spectacular crescendo of firecrackers riddles the night sky with glorious color. Digital cameras flash all around me. I smile haphazardly as I'm yanked this way and that for a picture draped with the brilliance of Philadelphia's vibrant backdrop. The New Year is officially here—with all its notorious sounds and excitement.

But amidst the commotion and anticipation of a new year, I feel stale, as if I have nothing to look forward to. At thirty years old, I've accomplished what some only wish to achieve in a lifetime. I have a high-paying job with great benefits and a long, important-sounding title. I drive a luxury car and own a three-bedroom home in the heart of the City of Brotherly Love. I buy anything I want whenever I want. I have enough clothes to fill two walk-in closets, enough shoes to line a grocery store aisle. I pay off my exorbitant credit card bills every month because I've driven myself enough to be able to afford to. I travel regularly, schedule weekly massages with a friend named Kate. I even have a housekeeper. People tell me I'm beautiful, ambitious, and successful—some even express how they envy me; but I'm beginning to see things differently. It's all a sham this life I've designed for myself. It's all for show.

Apart from my comfortable lifestyle, I've been blessed with an amazing family: the greatest parents anyone could ask for—the definition of unconditional love. My father, Reverend Tony Cavelli, is senior pastor of an Assemblies of God church in central New Jersey. He's been in the ministry ever since I can remember. He and Mom have served God with all their hearts, souls, and minds from the time I was three years old. I was raised in the church, amid the kinship and camaraderie of a church family—brothers and sisters in Christ—joined in unity as "the body."

But despite my upbringing, I decided that I didn't want Jesus. I didn't think I needed Him. Instead I opted to depend on myself and the illusions of this world. I chose the road more heavily traveled; the self-absorbed path where all twists, turns and bends led to my own gratification.

Thankfully, Mom and Dad have been patient with me, praying for me daily; even during the times I made choices that affected my whole family. The most notable of all was when, at the age of sixteen, only two years after my father was elected to pastor his first church, I gave birth to my son, Domenic. My pregnancy was a major scandal. Teenage pregnancies happened to girls without fathers, girls who didn't feel loved. That wasn't me. I was the apple of my dad's eye. I can't remember a day when he didn't tell me he loved me, when he didn't tell me I was the prettiest girl he'd ever laid eyes on—even to this day. The events surrounding Domenic's birth were rough for me, for my whole family, but we survived. Now, Domenic is such a huge part of our lives.

Mom and Dad remind me often that it was only through God's grace. But in spite of the evident grace demonstrated to me, I never acknowledged God's hand in it all. I never trusted Him. Instead I put my trust in me and in the world, hoping that I would eventually find the love and security for which I longed in my travels or work or possessions. But all the while, as I climbed corporate ladders and struggled to keep up with the world's system, I knew there was something missing, a void that money and prestige and success could never fulfill.

The pop of a champagne cork and the bellow of obnoxious laughter interrupt my thoughts. *What am I doing here?* I suddenly wonder as I watch a variety of meaningless events unfold around me. *Is this what life's all about? Things? Money? Parties?*

Vanities, I think to myself. It's all vanity.[i] There has to be more to life than this.

I look at my watch; it's four minutes past midnight. I wonder where my parents are, what they're doing. Most likely they're on their knees at church, welcoming the new year in prayer. It was there—at church, I'm sure of it—where I last saw smiles that were truly happy. And for the first time in many years, I wish I were there with them.

I'm on my own tonight. Domenic is with his father (we alternate holidays), and Gregory, my boyfriend—ex-boyfriend as of last night—is in New York with his friend Edward. He's attending a benefit dinner in Manhattan's Millennium Broadway Hotel, an all-expense-paid New Year's Eve getaway that I backed out of six hours before we were scheduled to leave. We had a terrible fight yesterday morning, over nothing, and I told him I never wanted to see him again. Funny thing is I meant it.

We've gone through this same breakup several times over the past year or so, but I'm sure this is the end. He hasn't even called to affirm his point of view and make some generic statement like, "We can work through this" or "It's just a minor setback." Or quote some line of poetry, as he does whenever he's really in the doghouse, something like, "The better days of life were ours…"[ii] That's how I know it's over.

We both said some unforgivable things, and I'm pretty sure we went too far to ever go back to a normal, respectable relationship. I can't remember exactly, but I think I called him a failure and a lowlife, just like his father—the two degrading identifiers I knew would hurt him the most. He usually puts me on probation for such outbursts, refusing to tell me he loves me, or ignoring me altogether for several hours. But no such probationary period was offered this time.

The line was certainly crossed; there's no going back now.

Gregory's a great person, incredibly smart and good looking, but just not the one for me. He's tall, six foot two, with curly, chestnut-brown hair that always seems too long; facial hair so dark that it appears his five o' clock shadow is more round the

I TOOK THE LONG WAY HOME

clock; luminous green eyes that glow with just a hint of sunlight; muscular physique, but not too much. He's stocky enough to make him just the right size. Simply one of those guys who hasn't a clue how attractive he really is, like movie-star attractive without the makeup artist or stylist—the perfect combination of clumsily sloppy and handsome. Sailor meets surfer meets attorney. Just my type.

Graduate of Georgetown Law, he earns a huge six figure salary each year in entertainment law, representing a variety of local celebrities: football players, up-and-coming rap artists—even a popular news anchor. He's a brilliant man. And not just about law. Politics. Prose. Science. Even cars. But with all he has going for him, he's miserably unhappy and irritable, oftentimes intolerable. I've never known anyone as smart and ambitious, yet so fearful of failure and rejection.

He has major familial issues. Mom's been addicted to anti-depressants for years while Dad's an alcoholic. Neither of them could ever hold a job. Gregory's enormously ashamed of them and he's stated on many occasions that he will never get married, ever. Still, I'm sure if I badgered him long enough, he'd cough up a sizeable ring, just for the experience. But we'd just end up divorced once we grew tired of each other.

It's only been two short years and the fantasy is over. We already have the itch for something new, something better. We're both alike in that way, too much alike: both looking for the next best thing. I guess that's what's wrong with most of our generation. We're all united by this major search for more.

With all these thoughts about Gregory, I drop my champagne flute. It crashes to the wood floorboards of the rooftop deck, shattering into tiny bits of glass; but no one notices. *Great*, I think to myself, because suddenly I decide it's time to go; I have to get out of this place.

I came here tonight in a cab with three friends—Kelly, Janette, and Sicily. Each girl is already paired with a guy she met at the last big social gathering we attended, and as I scan the balcony before making my great escape, I spot each girl snuggling with her man. *No need for goodbyes*, I decide.

I start toward a pair of sliding glass doors.

I'm halfway there when Dave, a gruff, lumbering man, grabs me. He probably thinks he's my friend since we traded smiles and small talk earlier this evening. I'd thought he was cute and somewhat interesting, but now it wouldn't matter if he were the reincarnation of John F. Kennedy Jr.; he'd better get his hands off me. "Where do you think _you're_ going?" he demands playfully.

I snap my arm away from him. He's had one too many beers, and I'm in no mood for playful games with a thirty-five-year-old child. "I'm leaving," I say.

"The party's just getting started." He moves closer.

"I have somewhere to go." I grimace.

"Why don't you stay?" His hand grazes my shoulder, and I suddenly feel like a piece of meat awaiting a slapdash slicing by an unqualified butcher.

"Don't ever touch me again." I shoot a lethal expression his way. He doesn't respond. Instead, he relents and I push forth toward the doors.

I make it into the house unscathed and head for the stairs. I hear voices over loud music and random laughter; and with each step, I feel a stronger urgency to run, run for my life.

As I retrieve my purse from a guest bedroom—an accessory that cost enough to feed a village in India for a year—I think of the shallow, empty person I've allowed myself to become. Surely no one here would ever believe I'm a preacher's daughter. They would never guess that I've been in church ever since I can remember. I attended Christian school for nine consecutive years; I can list the books of the Bible starting from Genesis and say them backward from Revelation by memory; I can recite dozens of Scriptures; and even discuss church doctrine intelligently with many Bible scholars. I've been to every kids' camp, youth camp, convention, and retreat. I listened to Christian music exclusively up until high school. I attended Bible studies and had family devotions every night—even on the weekends. My parents raised me in the church, trained me up in the way I should go, and trusted that I would never depart from it.[iii] But I have. In every way I've moved from the Lord.

For many years, as a child, I clung to Jesus and His Word just as Mom and Dad modeled. Saved when I was just six years old at the altar of the church in which I grew up, I loved the Lord with all my heart until the age of thirteen—when other _things_ got in the way, blurring my vision of Jesus. Now, at thirty, my Christian faith is only a memory. I sold my birthright for a fleeting taste of sin.[iv] Instead of God's perfect gift of salvation, I chose to chase the wind, searching for life and love in things and people, not realizing that a life devoted to things is a dead life.[v]

Purse in hand, I reach the first floor of Damian's lavishly decorated condominium and see a sprinkling of people loitering beside the food table. To my surprise, I recognize a girl I knew while growing up. We attended the same piano school for years. She had an awful hacking cough all while I knew her. I remember so distinctly watching her fingers stiffen and her face turn red as an apple midway into a piano recital as she released several foghorn-like coughs. I'd know her face anywhere—it's the name that escapes me. Christine or Kristen—maybe Kirstie. Doesn't matter. It looks like she's leaving, and I need a ride.

"Hi," I exclaim, walking over to her, optimistic that she'll recognize me.

She sees me, and her eyes instantly widen. "Stephanie?" she asks in disbelief. "Oh my gosh, how are you?"

"Doing well. How are you?" I ask, hugging her halfheartedly.

"You're the last person I'd expect to see here," she says. "I thought you went to church or something on New Year's."

I stifle a laugh. Of all the things she could remember about me, she recalls my churchgoing on New Year's. "No," I tell her. "I've been living in sin the past fifteen years, give or take a few summer Bible studies."

Her lips tighten. It's clear she doesn't know how to respond. *Living in sin* is a phrase used by born-again Christians, like *backsliding*, but it means nothing to this girl. If her frightened eyes could speak they'd ask if I was on drugs or maybe involved in satanic worship or prostitution. I'm sure nothing else in her mind would merit a life of sin other than the major, categorically bad sins committed in public. Damage control is clearly needed.

"I'm kidding," I say to ease the anxiety unfolding in each unanswered moment. "But, yeah, as a kid I spent every year at church with my parents. I'm surprised you remember."

Her face brightens. "How can I forget? You were the only kid who never saw the ball drop."

A burst of laughter escapes. "Well, Mom and Dad didn't think the ball was that important."

"How are your parents? Are they still into the whole church thing?"

"Yep, still into it. They're there now, and I'm here, wishing I were with them," I say, checking my watch. "I was actually hoping to find a ride home. I know catching a cab will take forever, but if I can get home and change, I can probably make it to their house in an hour or so."

"We're just about to leave—I can give you a ride."

"Are you sure?" I say, as if I didn't plan on asking.

"No problem," she says.

Perfect.

As I interlace methodically through an assortment of people, waving good-byes and offering lackadaisical excuses for my sudden departure, I see pairs of depleted eyes staring back at me, and I can't help but think of the only truly happy people I know. Several faces run through my mind—all churchgoers, firm believers in Christ. Their eyes are like stars in my mind, twinkling with a hope that perhaps someday I could have that same glow.

Could it be? I ask myself. Could my parents have been right all along—that following Jesus is the only way? All this time I thought I was so much better off than my parents, free from the rigid laws of religion and conventionality. Could it be that all along, I was the slave—to sin and its selfish desires? Could it be that the greatest liberty of all was right there in God's Word?

I finally make it out the front door, but Christine or Kristen is still inside looking for her boyfriend, Kevin.

Waiting, I use my cell phone to dial Dad's office at the church. I can hear the distant rumble of firecrackers as the phone rings. Then rings again. And again.

As the voicemail begins, I hang up, disappointed. I remind myself that if they're still at church, neither Mom nor Dad would be hanging out in the church office.

Just as I begin to dial Mom and Dad at home, the front door of Damian's condo opens and I hear music spill out. Christine or Kristen emerges with her boyfriend. He's tall and lanky, dressed in a silk shirt with tight-fitting jeans. Seeing him walk toward me, I slip my phone into my purse and try to look friendly. He throws his arm around me and steers me in the direction of the parking lot. "So I hear you went to music school with Christine." *So that's her name! I knew I was close.* Now if I can only get this guy's heavy arm off me.

"We're heading to a party in West Chester. Wanna come?" he asks.

I hear Christine's footsteps behind us. She scurries next to her man and grabs his hand. "She's meeting her parents," Christine answers for me.

"So what? It's New Year's. Tell Mommy and Daddy you got hung up."

"I really want to see them," I say. "Thanks anyway." I duck out from underneath Kevin's arm as Christine takes the lead toward the parking lot.

Just as we reach the car, a freezing rain starts. Kevin unlocks the driver's-side door first and hops in, leaving us ladies waiting in the cold and rain. From inside, he unlocks our doors. We hurry in, but it's cold and damp inside too. His shaky hand pushes the key into the ignition as Christine blasts the heat.

Kevin finally gets the car moving as the two of them talk about their next adventures of the night. They plan to party-hop till dawn. Gregory and I did that last year, and I remember being just as disappointed with that experience as I am with this year's. I'm tired of this, I decide, tired of being disappointed. Something has to change.

Kevin cranks up the radio so loud I wouldn't be able to hear a siren if it were in the trunk. He hasn't bothered asking where I live—maybe he's clairvoyant. Well, I can't take the chance. I tap his shoulder. He nods his recognition, but doesn't turn down the radio. I tap again, harder. His mouth moves, but I can't hear anything. I wedge myself between the two front seats and turn down the volume. They both scrunch their faces at me.

"What's wrong?" Christine asks.

"Do you have any idea where I live?" I ask Kevin.

The genius shakes his head, and I give him the address.

"Do you know where that is?"

"I'll find it," he assures me, then cranks up the stereo again.

I want to throw him out of the car at this point, but that would just delay my getting home. I'd better just sit tight.

Kevin's car finally pulls up to the large brownstones that comprise my street. Although I tell him where to stop, he still manages to drive past the house. There's now a car behind us so he can't back up. He offers to go around the block but I decline. I'd rather walk the extra few feet in the rain than have to tolerate the music any longer. "Thanks for the ride," I say, climbing out of the backseat.

I dash to the front door, avoiding two large puddles.

Entering my empty house, I smell the fresh aroma of vanilla potpourri left earlier by my housekeeper Sue. The house is warm, seventy-two degrees, and immaculate—just the way I like it. I zip off my wet, uncomfortable boots and exhale as I feel the soft, cushioned rug beneath my feet. I drop my purse and keys on a coffee table in the foyer, grab my cell phone from the pocket of my leather jacket, and dive for the couch.

Noticing the time, almost one AM, and realizing my chances of getting to my parents' New Jersey home before they both fall asleep are slim, I try them at home.

Dad answers on the first ring. His voice is sweet and gentle.

"Hi, Daddy."

"Steph!" he exclaims. "Happy New Year honey!"

"Happy New Year to you too."

"We missed you at church."

"I missed you too."

"Mom and I just got home. We prayed for you." Any other time, I'd sigh at the notion of them praying for me, because I, of all people, certainly do *not* need prayer. But tonight it's okay. In fact, it's wonderful.

"Thanks, Dad," I say. "I need it. Can I talk to Mom?"

"Sure," he says. "Love you."

I smile again. In all my life, he's never hung up the phone without assuring me he loves me. Even during the worst times growing up; when my heart was full of war and rebellion, he always told me he loved me. Even when it was the last thing he wanted to say, when there were a host of other more appropriate things to say.

"Love you, too, Dad."

I hear him hand the phone to Mom.

"What," she says sternly. I figure by the tone of her voice that she's still peeved from our earlier conversation. If I remember correctly I laughed condescendingly when she asked if I'd be at church. My answer was something like, "I think I've gone to enough church services to last a lifetime." Funny how a few hours can change a person's entire perspective.

"I'm sorry about earlier," I say.

She's quiet for a moment. "Is that all?"

"No," I pause, "what are you guys doing?"

"You know what we're doing, the same thing we do every year."

"Do you mind if I come over?"

"Come over? For what? I thought you'd be out partying."

"Not tonight."

"Have you talked to Poppy (their nickname for Domenic)?"

"Yeah, earlier. They went to see the fireworks."

There's a moment of silence. "Are you okay?" she asks.

I TOOK THE LONG WAY HOME

"Yeah, I'm fine."

"Then why do you want to come over?"

"I just wanted to spend time with you and Dad."

"You should have come to church. It's late now."

"I know, but I really want to see you guys."

"What's this about, Steph?"

Glad she finally asked I take a deep breath. "I, uh, had a revelation tonight, Ma—a New Year's revelation."

She doesn't respond.

"I was at this party and something happened to me, something I can't quite explain. It was like my eyes were opened to something I'd been blind to." I feel like a little kid telling my mommy about what I did at school. "I was with all these people, and it was like I could see inside them. Like I could feel their unhappiness."

Mom remains quiet.

"Ma, I don't want to live like this anymore. I feel hollow, almost like I'm dead inside." My hands begin to shake; my lips quiver. "I don't want to feel this way for the rest of my life." An unusual feeling wells up from the pit of my stomach as the words spill from my mouth. My eyes fill with tears. "I just…"

That's all I can manage without bursting into tears.

"Are you there?" Mom asks.

One whimper escapes.

"You always did think the world had something better for you," she says softly. "You searched your whole life. But like Dad and I have told you since you were a little girl, the things out there mean nothing. They'll never give you the peace you're looking for. Only Jesus can."

I listen, silently agreeing with my mother for the first time in many years.

"His Word's been in your heart since you were a little girl," she reminds me. "And I believe as you get older, you'll cling to it as Dad and I have. But you have to open your heart and seek Him first.[vi] You've done the opposite. You've sought after all these other things. Now it's time to be the woman God wants you to be."

"So what am I supposed to do?" I ask.

"Pray. Tell the Lord how you feel. Tell Him exactly what you just told me."

"I can't."

"Then you'll continue to feel empty."

Mom's right. I know what I have to do, and there's not a thing she can do to help.

"Look, Steph, it's almost one AM. I'm tired."

"Please don't go. I need to talk."

"There's Someone else waiting to hear from you. I'll call you in the morning."

The phone clicks off. She's gone.

I hang up, humbled, and curl under the leopard-print, velour blanket draped over my couch. Tears run down my face as I sit in the darkness of my living room and think of the words my father told me while I was growing up, the Scripture by which he modeled his life: "Seek ye first the kingdom of God and His righteousness, and all these things shall be added unto you."[vii] I've sought after all the other things first. But what have they profited me? I've sown to the wind. Gained the whole world but lost my soul.[viii]

I decide Mom's right; I need to pray.

I kneel beside the couch, bury my soaked face in a cushion, and talk to the Son of God.

"Lord, I've known about You since I was a little girl. I learned how You died so that I could have life. But I always thought there was something better in the world. So instead of seeking You, I put me first and forgot You. But I'm tired now; tired of living this shallow, empty existence. I need Your help, Lord. I can't do it on my own anymore. I need to know that You're here and that You care. I need to know Your will for my life. Please forgive me and come into my heart again. Fill me with the joy I had as a young girl. Show me the way, Lord. I need You now more than ever."

Wiping the tears from my face, I feel something unfamiliar: a calming peace that warms me, a peace that has been missing in my life for a long, long time. As I kneel beside the couch, basking in the peace that is unmistakably from the Lord, I decide it's time to start my life over from the beginning; but this time, with Christ as the center.

2

About Face

The hardest part about starting over with Christ as the center is the starting over part.

For me it was more than changing my lifestyle. People change the way they live all the time for health reasons, diets, relational commitments; I had to change my heart, my intentions, my entire way of thinking. It had to be a complete transformation. I wanted to be made new, afresh; stop whatever I was doing, change the direction in which I was going, and make a complete turnaround. I needed to be reborn.

To that end, the weekend after New Year's I resolved to cleanse my house of all the worldly contents I had accumulated during the course of my life without Christ. Things. Music. Books. Anything that could distract me from my newfound commitment to follow Jesus exclusively. I would purge my house of all secular influences. If I was going to change, my surroundings had to change. Even the little things. Everything had to go.

It was a cold Saturday morning in January when I conducted the massive cleanout that I would eventually look back on as my material day of surrender; so cold I'd slept with my socks and flannel pajama pants. The clock on my nightstand read 5:47 AM when I awoke and a surge of adrenaline ran through my body that I hadn't felt in a long time—not since I'd trained for the neighborhood five-mile run, in which I placed 134th in 145 runners.

This is the day I leave the world behind, I thought as I sat up in bed, stretching my arms high up toward the ceiling, craning my neck to relieve the tension left over from a tentative night of sleep. *Well, maybe I won't leave it all behind in one day,* I rethought, but it would certainly be the start of a long and arduous journey that no longer required the sole effort of one woman. Now there were two of us.

As I rose from the bed, somewhat shaky in the knees, I spotted two magazines on my bureau that needed to make their way to the garbage immediately, the trashy kind about the love lives of celebrities that are set out strategically near the checkout lane in grocery stores. For years I'd carefully studied the women on those pages, mainly to copy their hair and clothes and makeup, but also in pure curiosity about a group of people who'd forgotten God. They looked so glamorous on the pages of those magazines. Embarrassingly, I idolized them. In some twisted, backwards way of thinking, I aspired to be them. But that morning I could barely stand the sight of them. Behind the expensive clothes and cars and jewelry were people whose eyes were as empty as mine had been—maybe more so—and at that moment, I couldn't imagine a life more lonesome than theirs. I immediately chucked them into a tall wastebasket. As I headed down the hall toward the stairs, I thought, *That will be the first of many household casualties.*

When I made it to the living room, I felt a crisp draft assault my ankles. It slithered through the threshold of my front door as the howl of winter blistered relentlessly against my old windows that so desperately needed replacing. The thought of dashing upstairs and crawling back into bed almost overpowered me. I had left it a minute, maybe two, ago; and the warmth of my thick, down comforter was surely preserved.

But I couldn't go back, couldn't delay my mission any longer. Instead I overrode the programmed temperature on my thermostat to eighty degrees, shoved my feet into wool slippers and threw on a heavy sweatshirt—one of Gregory's that fit like a parka but felt like a blanket.

Typically, when it was my weekend with Domenic, I'd wake him up early on Saturday, about eight AM, to have him help with chores and then embark on some spontaneous excursion, like the zoo or aquarium or even, during wintertime, snowboarding. I'd often plan road trips to Manhattan or Baltimore or Washington DC for a day of sightseeing and activities on our Saturdays together. Some mothers could let their kids sleep until noon, but I never could. To me, sleeping after eight AM on a Saturday was a waste, like using a sick day for a cold or headache.

Some mornings were harder than others to wake him. Usually I'd saunter into his room and just tell him it was time to get up and he would—no problem. Other times I'd have to resort to more maternal methods. I'd amble in his room, after getting no response or reaction from my verbal commands, crawl into his bed, squirm under his nautical-themed comforter and lean my cheek on his. His body would be warm like an electric blanket, sprawled out in the bed like a starfish. "Wake up,

sleepyhead," I'd whisper teasingly, "we have a lot to do today..."
He'd grumble and roll over, yank his comforter away from me
and pile it over his head.

Other mornings I'd just sit at the edge of his bed and marvel
at how beautifully he'd grown, how he'd evolved from this little
boy who'd follow me around the house like a shadow, vying for
any second of my attention, repeating "mommy" hundreds of
times during the day—even if I was looking directly at him.
"Mommy look at that" or "Mommy, listen to this." "Mommy,
mommy, mommy."

"What?" I'd finally shriek. He'd gulp hard and then jabber
about nothing for several minutes, stuttering and stammering all
the way, almost too excited to speak. He'd talk until no air was
left in his lungs and then take a long, deep breath to restart. It
seemed that overnight he morphed into this teenager with huge
feet, an unrecognizable voice and the appetite of a horse.

Now, on quiet mornings while Domenic slept in, I'd sneak
into his room and tickle the heels of his size ten feet, which
dangled from the twin-sized bed he'd clearly grown out of, and
scratch his large hands, which rested lifelessly at the side of the
bed. When he began to stir, I'd wonder, *Where did the years go?*

Domenic and I had practically grown up together. Born
when I was just sixteen, he was like a little brother to me. For
years he woke me up on weekends. It was as if his internal alarm
clock blasted at six AM every Saturday, as if some voice called to
him and said, "It's time to wake up Mommy."

I would be sleeping in my room and hear a loud *boom,* like a
bowling ball falling off a shelf, and realize that it was Domenic
falling to the floor after climbing out of his crib. I'd then hear the
swoosh sound of his diaper as his swift little legs wandered down
the hall to my room. He'd burst open my door, the knob
crashing into the wall, and march right up to my bed, as if I
wasn't allowed to sleep while he was awake. "Mommy," he'd say
as he pressed his face against mine, "Me 'wake." I'd feel his wet
lips against my nose, his bushy hair scratching my eyelids. This
would be my first wake-up call, with several more attempts to
follow. I'd tell him to play with his toys, which he'd do for no
more than five minutes before trying again. If only he knew that
his mommy was a teenager who just wanted to talk on the phone
all night and sleep until noon. "Mommy, me all done pwayin',"
he'd say. I'd tell him to try to go back to sleep. "But me not
tired," he'd assure me. Everything inside me wanted to tell him

to scram—and sometimes I would. But as his warm, pudgy nose grazed across mine, and his dark, honest eyes gazed at me, I couldn't help but lift him into bed with me and gnaw him like an ear of corn.

He was just as adorable as a teenager—a little mouthy, but still cute. I couldn't help but creep into his room on those quiet mornings and peck his cheeks with kisses. Maybe part of me wanted to recapture those moments when I was just a teenager; times I almost always traded for more sleep.

But I had other plans for our Saturday this week. It was cleanout day—and if he didn't wake up on his own, I'd be sure to enlist his assistance in the next few hours.

The house was in its usual condition a week after our housekeeper's visit: a disaster area. One thing neither Domenic nor I possessed was neatness. Our stuff was everywhere. Shoes. Coats. Scraps of gift wrap left over from Christmas. Even a few ornaments that never made it into any of the storage boxes we packed the day after New Year's. Visitors would think a family of ten lived there.

I had no plan of attack for my cleanout. With a set of various-shaped boxes and extra-large trash bags I hauled up from the basement, I began my mission with only a scattered sense of direction. Emptying drawers and picking apart shelves, I realized so much had to go.

The CDs went in the trash—even my favorites—music I used as sedatives for broken hearts and broken dreams and even death. Knowing Jesus would replace my need for such things, I chucked them like old stereo equipment, hearing them clank and crash as they fell atop one another. The CDs I'd often commanded Domenic never to touch were discarded. They were a reminder of the past, of my dependence on anything other than God. I didn't feel the least bit grieved to part with them. They belonged to someone else, part of a former life that no longer existed.

I removed two shelves of books, beautifully written novels with pages satiated in adultery and promiscuity, lying and deceit. One by one, I trashed them. I went through no less than fifty. In addition were several self-help guides with the conjectural hero being oneself. *You can do it all!* No wonder I'd felt such an extensive hollowness. For years I filled my heart with the lies of men, believing that I could depend on my own strength and that of my fellow man. It was no wonder depression set in so frequently. My life depended on the fallibility of humans.

But it was now time for a new Driver, an infallible Voyager, One with power to calm storms and part waters. It was time to give up the controls, the self-help myths and quick fixes, and get on board with the Master.

Useless hardbacks had replaced the only Book I really needed, the definitive survival guide for a lost and dying world: the Bible. As I went through my shelves, I saw it, all alone, dumped in a practically unreachable area. It lay flat on the top shelf, removed from the more "useful" books. I stretched up as high as I could reach on my toes, slid it from its place on the shelf, and brought it down. A coating of dust evidenced its neglect. I ran my fingers across the green leather cover. The dust rolled onto my hands like black powder, as the gold engraved title showed through: *Holy Bible*. I hesitated for a moment before opening it, anticipating the truth I'd find inside.

I opened the thick cover; the stiff, bound pages crinkled as I turned to the dedication. Black cursive writing covered the top quarter of the page. My dad had written this message:

> *Steph,*
>
> *Live for Jesus. That's all that matters.*
> *Love you, Dad*

I smiled. Even at thirty, Dad still advised me with one of his famous lines: "Live for Jesus." My brother and I had heard it at least a million times. I'd ask him the most difficult question, confer about the most urgent situation, and the best he could come up with was "Live for Jesus."

I remember being ten years old, running into our old row home in Philadelphia, stringy blonde hair dangling to my waist, wailing about some seemingly dire event that had happened. I found my father on the couch, smiling peacefully, with the Bible open on his lap.

"Dad, Dad, Dad!" I yelled frantically as I stumbled into the house. My dad's eyes lifted as I approached him, patting his knee with my hand. "This boy from around the corner said I looked like a vampire," I said, my voice squeaking. "He said my teeth look like fangs!" I stood there, catching my breath, slowly calming at just the sight of my dad's reassuring eyes. I waited for his response, hoping he'd offer an equally insulting remark to quell this evil boy's sinful accusation, or at least damn him to hell for all eternity; but no. I should have known better.

Dad tilted his head and said, "Live for Jesus, Steph. That's all that matters."

"But Dad." I stomped my feet on the carpeted floor. "What about the boy? Don't you care?"

"The Lord doesn't look at the outward appearance, Steph. He looks at the heart."[ix]

I got so angry. All Dad cared about was God. He loved God more than me.

That's what I thought when I was younger, and what I knew was true now. He loved what could never be taken from him. He loved his God more than anything. More than his wife, more than his children. Dad knew that children were gifts and could be taken back at any moment. His job was to get our souls ready for eternity. This life was merely a dry run, a whisper, when compared with eternity, and Dad knew it. Living for Jesus was the best advice he could give me.

"Trust in the Lord" was another one of Dad's favorite one-liners. "Our hope is found in Christ alone." "Only if the Lord wills." We couldn't go food shopping unless the Lord willed. And that was just the start. Dad had all kinds of scripturally based answers and explanations.

While growing up I went through stages of thinking he knew everything to nothing, to everything again. But regardless of what I thought, Dad never swayed or wavered in his convictions. I hated him for it then, but now I admire him more than any other man I've ever met.

By the time Domenic trudged down the stairs from bed, with his hair pressed to his head on one side and frizzy and stiff on the other, the living room was in disarray. Empty shelves. Packed boxes. Filled trash bags. If he didn't know any better, he would have thought we were moving. In a way we were.

"What are you doing?" he asked in a groggy voice that sounded nothing like his own.

I hadn't told him about my revelation; I had barely seen him the past few days between his visits with his father and then with Mom and Dad. But I knew it was time for the announcement.

"I have something important to tell you," I said as he traipsed past the boxes and plopped onto a chair at the kitchen table. I followed him into the kitchen and sat in the chair across from him. His eyes were half open, and he looked as if he could rest his head on the table and go right back to sleep.

He cupped his chin in his hands and tried to look attentive. "Well?"

"I've given my heart to Jesus," I said matter-of-factly, folding my hands in confidence. I didn't need to explain what this meant or how it affected my life; Domenic knew. He'd grown up in church. As much time as he spent with my parents, he'd probably been to about the same number of church services I'd been to at his age. He had asked Jesus to come into his heart when he was five years old.

Domenic often asked me why I didn't want to go to church on Sundays, or why we weren't "church people" like Mom-Mom and Pop. "That's their thing," I'd told him. Or I'd say that we could be Christians without having to go to church every Sunday.

He asked me one time if I loved Jesus.

"Of course," I answered.

"Then why don't you visit His house?"

I laughed to myself and wondered where he heard that: no doubt at Sunday school or children's church.

Poor Domenic had watched me straddle the fence for years in my struggle to find my identity and locate the true reason for living. If ever there was a poster child for lukewarm Christianity it was me. I proclaimed it as my religion but never lived it. I talked the talk but didn't walk the walk, preached but never practiced. It was only by God's grace that He didn't spew me from His mouth years ago.[x]

But this time was different.

Domenic lifted his chin from his hands and asked, "When did this happen?"

"New Year's Eve," I said. "I was at this party and I heard the Lord speak to me."

"What did He say?"

"He told me that I could never find peace apart from Him."

"What else did He say?"

"That He wanted my life. My heart, my soul. And that I'm nothing without Him."

"Isn't that a Bible verse?"

"Yes," I said, remembering John 15:5, one of the many verses I'd memorized as a child: *"I am the vine; You are the branches… Apart from me you can do nothing."*

"I thought so." He stretched his mouth open for a yawn. "Did you tell Mom-Mom and Pop about what happened?" he drawled as his mouth relaxed back to form.

"Yes."

"What about Gregory?" he asked, rubbing his fingers across his eyes.

"I haven't told him yet."

"Does this mean you have to break up with him?"

Domenic was no fool. He'd heard Gregory's cursing, seen the drinking, knew all about Gregory's love for money and prestige, a blatant lust for all the world had to offer. Over the last two years, Domenic saw many sides of Gregory: the generous man who'd never allow me to pay for anything; the baseball player who taught him how to throw a "killer" curve ball; the studious lawyer who'd work through the night on our kitchen table and leave for the office long before my alarm clock rang; the entrepreneurial risk taker who'd purchased two farms in western Pennsylvania in hopes of developing real estate; the spontaneous jokester who thought it'd be fun to take my ninety-year-old great grandmother who couldn't see, walk, or hear to the rodeo. Domenic also saw the temper in Gregory, the man who punched a hole through our dining room wall after losing big on a Super Bowl bet, the man who went months without talking to his mother because she forgot my birthday. He saw many things in Gregory, good and bad, but never saw Christ in him. He never saw the things he'd seen in his grandparents, the qualities exuded by people who truly followed Christ.

As I sat there that morning, planning my answer, I wondered if Domenic would miss Gregory. Would he miss the man who had fused his life into ours? It didn't matter. Gregory no longer had a place in our lives. I just needed to let Domenic know that.

"I already broke up with him," I answered, nervously squeezing a ripened banana that lay on our kitchen table.

"When?" he asked.

"The night before New Year's Eve." I peeled the banana carefully, awaiting a plethora of questions. Sometimes it felt like Domenic was my father. He always needed to know my business. I often wondered, in my deliberate attempts to conceal my vulnerability to him—to persuade him that I'd always maintained control over every situation—if I'd come across even more vulnerable and defenseless. It seemed like he worried about me more than I worried about him.

I TOOK THE LONG WAY HOME

Sure enough, the questions came. Where were we when I broke up with Gregory? Was it before or after I gave my heart back to the Lord? What did he say? Was he mad?

I answered all of my son's questions and told him that Gregory was not *the one*. He asked what I meant by *the one*. "I just don't think the Lord ever wanted us to be together."

"Did you want to marry him?" he asked.

I hesitated, wanting to answer truthfully. "No."

Domenic scrunched his eyes, pondering my simple response, no doubt searching for a hidden meaning. "Then why did you bother being his girlfriend?"

"I shouldn't have," I told him before he could ask any more questions.

"So we're not gonna see him anymore?"

"Maybe once in a while," I said, "but not like we used to."

He sighed, visibly disappointed. Gregory may not have been the best person in the world, the most ideal candidate for a stepfather, but he was a decent man, and he genuinely cared for Domenic.

"I'm sorry." I reached across the table to hold his hands. "But there's no way I can be a Christian if I stay with Gregory."

He nodded. "I know."

"I'm really sorry, Dom."

"It's okay," he said, releasing a long sigh, his eyes heavy and downcast.

"I never meant for you to be hurt," I said.

"I'm not," he assured me, but not convincingly. "I just..." He paused. "I just want to know one thing."

"What?" I rubbed his dry, warm hands.

"Can you make me some breakfast? I'm really hungry."

I stretched my torso across the table and hugged him. He always knew how to make light of a situation—even the ones that hurt the most.

The following Sunday, when Domenic was with his father for the weekend, I found myself in the place where I'd started life: church. Not in the safety of my parents' church, where I could sneak in late, sit beside Mom, and slip out early, but the church in which I was raised. The place where I first accepted Jesus into my heart. The place where I felt my first convictions. I wanted to remember that place, that building, that altar—go back to the beginning and start fresh.

Apart from two funerals and one wedding, it had been almost fifteen years since I last visited; and when I entered the building, it felt good to be back home.

The building was spiked with the smell of the past, my childhood, a time when youth and innocence equated happiness. A sensation of nostalgia momentarily froze me at the door as I took in the scent and recalled cherished memories.

Recognizing my temporary immobility, I willed myself back to the present and moved inside. The sanctuary looked exactly as I remembered. Shaped like an oyster, with high ceilings, white walls, and royal blue Berber rugs laced with flecks of black, it was divided into four large sections of chairs that all faced the platform where the same wooden podium from which Dad had preached on countless Sundays stood as the central landmark of the room. The black lacquered piano on which I'd learned my first musical chords still stood to the right of the podium, with the organ on the left. The baptismal, with its ornate, stained-glass backdrop and the tub in which I was baptized at age twelve with my brother, Michael, then age eleven, loomed behind the choir seats, disguised with a royal blue curtain and arrangement of white poinsettias. Everything was just as I remembered—like a faded photo restored from the archives of my memory.

I saw many familiar faces, faces that hadn't changed a bit in fifteen years—people who'd attended church their whole lives. It was almost as if I had passed through a time capsule. I'd ambled out the doors as a skinny, unkempt kid with blue jeans, sneakers, and sweatshirt, and returned as a refined, heel-wearing blonde with lipstick and perfume. I had grown up, while my former home church and family, for the most part, remained the same. I assumed no one would recognize me. Who had really noticed the awkward teen who bumbled around these parts like an escaped inmate anyway?

I found out quickly that they had noticed. And they indeed remembered me.

"Do you know who that is?" someone whispered as I breezed by. "That's Pastor Tony's daughter."

"Did you see that girl?" another said. "She's Tony Cavelli's daughter. Remember Pastor Tony and his wife?"

All around I saw eyes light up at the sight of me, as if I were the daughter of a celebrity.

I scurried past them, unready to discuss my former life with those who knew me as the sweet, innocent pastor's daughter who jabbered through Sunday morning services with her friends in the first row, passing notes and giggling. After my pregnancy scandal, I figured most people had written me off as a hopelessly immoral backslider, doomed to hell with all the other unreformed sinners. I half expected some of the older saints or deacons on standby at the entrances with Bibles and offertory plates to escort me out at any moment.

But the reality was just the opposite. Everyone was kind and loving, grabbing me by the arm for hugs, squeezing my face for kisses, telling me how they loved me, my family, even my son, whom they'd never met. "How's your father? And your mother? It's so good to see you."

One of my father's good friends, Mark, a lifetime member of the church, got hold of me not long after I entered. He was short and stocky, the image of first-generation Italy, with dark skin and white hair. He was dressed in a gray pinstriped suit, at least a head shorter than me, with glasses that covered most of his face. "How are you, gorgeous?" he asked with a grin, squeezing my cheeks together so my lips bubbled out.

He then whisked me clear across the sanctuary and led me to the last row on the far right side; quite noticeably his row, where he, his wife and family sat thirteen years ago and for probably twenty years before that. "Do you know who this is?" he asked a bystander whose face I'd never seen. "This is Tony Cavelli's daughter; he used to be the assistant pastor here." The man nodded kindly, as if he knew my father, though his eyes revealed that he hadn't a clue. I smiled back, equally clueless as to the identity of the person looking at me, but feeling proud nonetheless.

Even at thirty, I was still Pastor Cavelli's daughter, identified on a last-name basis. But for the first time ever, I was proud of it. Like the prodigal son returning to his father's home after living in squalor with pigs, I'd returned to my father's home with a repentant heart and great expectation for my new journey with Christ. No longer did I feel ashamed of being a pastor's daughter. I'd hated it as a young girl, when I longed to be like everyone else and not any different, but no more. No longer did I feel I had something to prove. I was a child of the King of kings and Lord of lords, and it was about time I started behaving as such.

The pastor's message was just what the Lord wanted me to hear. He spoke about being born again, dying to the old sinful nature and being born in Christ as a new creation.

He spoke about unconditional surrender, allowing nothing to remain from the old self. I knew that's what I needed to do: surrender myself to Christ. Everything. My hopes. Dreams. Fears. Failures. My whole life.

I wanted someone I could count on for all those things, someone who would never let me down. I wanted to dump my burdens at the Cross, build my house on the Rock. When the rains and floods and storms of life came, I'd remain standing, structurally and spiritually.[xi] I wanted that peace that passes all understanding.[xii] And now I knew for sure where to find it.

To think, all along, while I searched the world for peace, the Answer was right there in that dusty Bible I ignored on my shelf. Right there in those words Mom and Dad had recited my entire life, in those prayers, those sermons. In Christ. It was in Him all along.

Dad's words were becoming clear to me now. Living for Jesus was really all that mattered.

I TOOK THE LONG WAY HOME

3

Sin Calling

When my phone rang at almost midnight, I thought, *Only two people call this late on a weeknight: my mother and Gregory.* Everything inside me wanted to throw the phone across the room and fall back into the deep sleep from which I was rudely awakened, but instead I reached over to turn on my lamp and collected my voice for a throaty hello.

"Hi, Steph," the deep voice on the other end said.

My stomach cramped in anxiety at the sound of his voice. It had been a whole month since I saw him or heard his voice, one full month since I rededicated my life to Jesus. If I had the nerve, I'd have told him to call back in a year—maybe then I'd be strong enough to talk to him. But I opted to stay on the line. "Hi, Gregory," I murmured.

"You sound annoyed," he said. "Did I wake you?"

"Yes." I remembered the countless times over the past two years when he'd call at this hour to tell me about an ingenious idea he'd come up with, or some documentary he'd watched on HBO, or how he couldn't sleep.

"I'm sorry," he said.

"It's okay."

"Been thinking about you lately. You guys okay?"

"We're fine," I assured him, cracking my knuckles.

"Are you sure?"

"Yeah, why?" I flopped over onto my stomach and settled into a pillow, wondering if he thought we wouldn't be okay without him.

"Just haven't heard from you since the night we broke up. No one has. I was beginning to think you'd died or something."

I have. The Stephanie that Gregory once knew had died and was born again. But how could I explain that to him? How could I tell him the one thing I'd disdained for much of the two years I'd known him was suddenly my life, my purpose?

"I've just been busy, keeping to myself," I said calmly. "How are you?" I asked in an effort to transition the conversation toward a subject he seemed to love the most in life: himself.

"Great," he said. "Never been better."

There was a certain blissfulness in his voice—it almost scared me.

"There's something I need to tell you, Steph," he said, his voice stepping up with bursts of excitement. "I met someone."

My heart thumped hard in my chest. The tone of his voice, the song in his words, made it clear that this *someone* meant something special to him. I didn't like it. But I had to admit the obvious: a guy like Gregory doesn't stay single long. "That's nice."

"Actually, I met the love of my life."

Love of his life. If my heart could sink from my chest and flop onto the floor, it would have. I wanted to scream and cry and laugh all at the same time. I didn't know what to say or think in that excruciating moment. But I knew I had to respond quickly to avoid any obvious sign of uneasiness.

"Again?" I asked sarcastically, remembering how loosely he'd used that phrase when he met me a few years earlier.

"This is different," he assured me. "This girl is it. She's incredible. And beautiful. And so smart. She's amazing." Although I wished he would stop, he continued. "We met on New Year's Eve. I was so upset about us that night, and there she was, this bombshell! We talked all night and we've been together practically every day since. I'm in love, Steph."

His words pummeled through me like an earthquake. Gregory had never used such complimentary words without consuming a considerably large portion of alcohol and he didn't sound drunk.

"Why are you telling me this?" I asked angrily, rolling over onto my back and peeling the blankets away from me.

"Because I asked her to marry me," he blurted excitedly. "And I didn't want you to hear it from anyone else."

His words cut through me like a knife. I couldn't believe what he was telling me.

"I thought you swore you'd never get married," I said, wondering how his mind changed in just one month.

"That's before I met Melanie, before I met a woman worth marrying."

I swallowed his words like a bitter pill.

"Thanks," I said, flattening a wrinkle in my bed sheet.

"No offense," he said nonchalantly. "It's just that Mel's more woman than any of my past girlfriends could ever be."

I TOOK THE LONG WAY HOME

Good old Gregory knew just how to throw the punches. A battle seethed inside me. My flesh screamed for retaliation. But my new self said to rejoice in all things;[xiii] love my enemies;[xiv] do good to those who hurt me.[xv] It took every ounce of faith to do so. "I'm happy for you," I uttered, biting my bottom lip hard. "I'm glad you finally found someone worth marrying." I concentrated on breathing slowly.

"That's not what you really want to say," he murmured with cynicism.

After exhaling, I answered calmly, "If you'd told me this a month ago I'd have called you all kinds of names. But things are different now. I've found someone too."

"Don't tell me," he said sarcastically. "He's *the one*, and he's more man than I can ever be."

"Yes. He's the one I've looked for all my life."

He chuckled, but I ignored him.

"I've found Jesus and He's all the man I need. He's a friend who sticks closer than any brother or sister or boyfriend ever could."[xvi]

"So your parents have finally gotten to you," he sneered.

"This has nothing to do with my parents."

"Sure it does. I told Mel about them, how they go to church so often. It's like their life."

"It is."

"And now they've managed to suck you into the whole religion thing."

"It's not about religion," I said. "It's about a relationship. My parents have a relationship with God, and now I've formed a relationship with Him too."

"Hey, if it makes you happy, go ahead and latch on to whatever your parents want you to."

"My parents can't get me into heaven, Gregory."

"Oh, so now you're going to heaven?" He laughed.

"Yes."

"Don't fool yourself. If heaven exists, you of all people will not be there."

"Sounds funny coming from someone who claims there are no certainties in life."

"Then I officially retract the statement. There are certainties in life, and one of them is that you will not be in heaven. You'll be burning in hell with the rest of us egocentric pessimists."

"Actually, I won't. And that's one thing I'm certain of."

"Well, I'm glad you're finally certain of something."

"I'm more than certain," I said with conviction. "I'm happy. I'm truly happy."

"Happiness was one thing I could never offer you."

"At least you can finally accept your inadequacy."

"I'll bet a year's salary you'll marry someone exactly like your father."

"I hope so." I grabbed a small photo album from my nightstand. "He's a wonderful man."

"That has nothing to do with it. If your father beat you, you'd marry a wife beater. If your father cheated on your mother, you'd end up with a womanizer."

"So I guess Melanie's a pill-popping drunk," I said, but instantly regretted it.

"Now, that's the Stephanie I know and love! You had me fooled there for a minute."

"I'm sorry," I murmured, flipping through photos of Gregory and me from Thanksgiving. "I shouldn't have said that."

"I'm impressed you held out this long."

"I can't say I've changed completely, but I'm getting there. I'm trying."

"Whatever works for you, Steph. Melanie and I are agnostics, so it really doesn't matter to us."

I stifled a laugh. Born and raised Catholic, Gregory was suddenly an agnostic. I guess he'd convert to Islam if *Mel* wanted him to.

"I'm happy you found Melanie," I said, realizing the love captured in the pictures I held was now obsolete. "It seems you two are a perfect match."

"I always thought you were *the one*," he said, almost sweetly. "And I do miss Domenic."

"He misses you too."

"He's a great kid. Deserves a lot better than me. He needs someone like your dad." He paused. "For what it's worth, I'm sorry things didn't work out with us. But it's a big responsibility, being a father...even a stepfather."

Funny, I thought, recalling the countless occasions he gushed about what a great kid Domenic was, *the responsibility never seemed to bother him before.*

"Listen, I have to go," he said. "I have an all-nighter tonight and Mel's moving in on Sunday."

I TOOK THE LONG WAY HOME

"Moving in?" I blurted, snapping the album shut.

"Yeah. We'll probably get married soon, so I figured we should move in together now."

Moving in. Marriage. Soon. At that moment it hit me: Gregory had really moved on. This wasn't a breakup, where we would each come to our senses in a week, or miss each other so much that we'd get back together despite our unhappiness. It was the end. The end of a relationship. A friendship. A oneness. I sensed a flood of emotion welling inside me as a tear rolled down my cheek. Maybe I wasn't as strong as I thought. Maybe losing Gregory meant more than I realized. I crinkled the bed sheet between my fingers and wiped my face, desperate to conceal any sign of weakness.

"I need to get rid of your stuff," he yanked me from my thoughts, oblivious to the damage he'd caused to my heart. "There's a bunch of Domenic's stuff here too. Some basketballs. A football. Think he wants any of them?"

I mustered my voice for a solid "No."

"I can drop them off; it's no problem."

I sucked air in hard. "No, thanks."

"I'm sorry it has to be this way, Steph. I really am. I'll always love you. And I love Domenic—you know that. I'll probably miss him the most. But I can't marry someone who has a kid with someone else."

I choked back the tears and almost shrieked in fury at his remark. Any tender or sorrowful thoughts I had about Gregory dissolved in that instant to a loathing so strong I wanted to slam the phone against the dresser until it crumbled in pieces.

"You're unbelievable." I hurled the album to the wall and watched as several photos tumbled out from their holders.

"I didn't mean it like that; you know I love him—"

"Don't. You. Dare—"

"I do!" he interjected.

"You have no idea what it means to love someone!"

"Like you do," he began.

"I have to go." I cut him off. "I've indulged your massive ego for two years at the price of my soul, and I just can't do it anymore."

I hung up. My heart racing. Hands shaking. The phone rang seconds after I put it down, but I quickly turned the ringer off and stuffed the phone under my mattress. I couldn't bear another conversation. Instead I fell to the floor on my hands and knees and began to pluck the remaining holiday photos of Gregory from their holders in the album and toss them onto the carpet with the others. Then, one by one I ripped his smiling face in two, sobbing and groaning, as quietly as I could as not to wake Domenic in the next room. I did so until there was nothing left but scraps of paper: the evidence of a broken heart.

And then it was quiet.

I stared blankly at the pile of torn photos. Gregory's hurtful words charged through my mind like a freight train. The room seemed to circle around me. I wondered what I could do to make the pain stop, what I could do to rid myself of Gregory forever. I prayed for strength.

At that moment I understood why God instructs His children to wait for marriage, wait for the person He has ordained to be our spouse. His motive is to keep us from hurt, to protect us from the anguish that comes from separation and rejection.

As I crouched on my floor, I remembered keenly how Mom and Dad had always urged me to keep myself pure. "Save yourself for your husband," Mom told me over and over. "The Lord has great plans for your life." I now understood why they wanted me to wait.

Though I was no longer the little girl Mom and Dad wished to keep pure and protected, I knew God could make me pure again—in heart and mind. Even in body.

Idling there beside those torn photos, my mind wandered back in time, recalling the stories my parents had told me about how they came to know Jesus Christ as their personal Lord and Savior.

4

Mom and Dad

My parents weren't always born again Christians. In fact, if there is such a scale that determines lesser or greater measures of grace, their testimony of transformation is far greater than mine could ever be.

They were married in 1974 and, at the time, Dad was a full-blown heroin addict. At the age of twenty-four, he had been in and out of four secular rehab centers, placed at several hospitals—even contracted Hepatitis C at the ripe old age of eighteen. He'd made his home at Horizons House, Community Drug Treatment Center, and St. Joseph's Substance Abuse, each for weeks on end, only to conclude his stay with the same futile outcome.

Dad and his family migrated to America from a small town in northern Italy when he was just eight-years-old. Dad's father, my Grandpa Cavelli, left the old country in search of a more prosperous future for his family: four children at the time and later, three America-born children. For him, the United States offered a home, education, and a steady income. But for my dad, America represented something other than stability and hope. There was a darker side to the Land of Opportunity that seemed to ingest Grandpa Cavelli's son. When he was a teenager, Dad latched onto the overindulgences of American culture, culminating a drug addiction that garnered catastrophic consequences and familial shame. "*Disgraziad*," Grandpa would say to him. "Disgrace." Dad's behavior was certainly disgraceful.

Mom was also lost, in her own way. She had no addiction problems, but she didn't know God. She came from a broken home, with parents whose mission in life was to spite each other. Screaming, cursing, fistfights, infidelity, and abandonment were just some of the things Mom and her siblings endured while growing up. On the surface, they appeared as the typical Italian-Catholic family, with a mother, father, and five kids. But they were far from normal.

Mom's parents married very young—Grandma Pinto was sixteen, and her dad, who I never knew as Grandpa, was twenty. Grandma had gotten pregnant prior to saying, "I do," and at that time, marriage was the cure for such a scandalous, shameful sin. In this case, it was like putting a Band-Aid on a gunshot wound. The two "lovebirds" were a terrible match.

"It was a volatile relationship," Mom told me. "They broke up and got back together so many times. One week they loved each other, the next week they hated each other. When they were together, they acted like newlyweds: kissing, holding hands, gazing at each other. But it never lasted. Unfortunately, nine months after their love fests, they'd have another kid."

Mom, along with her brother and sisters, had lived in more than twenty houses while growing up. "One time, when I was twelve years old," she shared with me, "I came home from school and couldn't get into my house. I looked in the window, and all the furniture was gone." Later that day, Mom found that my grandmother had moved without telling any of them—including her husband.

As a child, my mother held on to a small glimmer of hope that her parents would change someday, that their lives would improve. But as the years progressed, instead of getting better, things grew worse. Following a vicious divorce, my grandparents left their children shattered in spirit and divided in habitat. Three of the children—my mother included—moved in with their grandparents, while the two youngest girls moved in with their mother and her new boyfriend. My mom was thirteen at the time. Two of her sisters were much younger—one still in diapers.

Two years after the divorce, Mom's father wanted to marry another woman. Since the Catholic leaders didn't permit a divorcé to be married in the church, he requested an annulment. It was granted. Five kids and twenty-two years of marriage were dissolved by a single piece of paper.

"He paid big money for that," Mom would say.

In hopes of gaining the family she never quite had as a child, Mom married Dad immediately after graduating high school. But she married a junkie and her hopes of a happy family were diminished by substances with names like methadone and heroin.

Shortly into the marriage, Mom was convinced she had married the devil. She knew she'd have to do something drastic to help him. With no money and minimal stability, she did what many young wives in marital turmoil did back then—she got pregnant. Not once, but twice in two years—back-to-back babies with a husband who could barely remember his own name.

Motherhood wasn't exactly the answer Mom thought it would be. Not even the responsibility of rearing two children could incite Dad to change.

Many interventions were implemented, all with the same results. Dad would agree to all kinds of conditions. But his promises to change, to get help, to be there for the family were empty—broken before the words even spilled from his mouth. He had been to every drug counselor, every rehabilitation center in the Philadelphia area; not one could fix him. He was a lost cause.

Mom's family tried to convince her to leave him—not only for her own good, but for the well-being of her children. "We'll all be better off," they told her. "It's best for everyone." But Mom had no job or education or career to fall back on. She had nowhere to go, no money for food or clothes. Her life had turned into a one-man circus, with Dad as the main attraction. Except she was the only person left in the audience, and all the love in the world couldn't keep her in the seat for one more show.

At that point, out of pure desperation, Mom called upon the name of the Lord.

She didn't know God or how to talk to Him. To her He was an obscure figure, hovering above the clouds in a place called heaven. She was sure He didn't care about her problems. Surely He had more important things to do.

But she cried out to Him anyway, in hopes that her plea would somehow make it to heaven. With faith as small as a mustard seed,[xvii] she asked Him to touch her husband, to heal him, to make him whole. To save her family. Perhaps, somehow, this God she had heard of would have compassion and lift her up from the pit of despair.

The Lord indeed saw her tears and heard her anguished cry. He initiated a chain of events that would lead to my parents' salvation and ultimate restoration.

Not long after Mom's talk with God, a friend of Dad's, a reformed drug addict, recommended he go to Teen Challenge, a Christian drug-rehabilitation program started by David Wilkerson in 1958—the largest and most successful program of its kind in the world. Mom decided it would be their last attempt at rehabilitation as a couple. If Teen Challenge didn't work, she would leave him, for good.

In 1979, Dad left home for Teen Challenge. Assuming it was like every other program he'd been to, Dad believed he could bamboozle the workers with his mastered confidence and clever speech. He would blame his addiction on his parents, his friends, the way he was raised, his feelings of inadequacy and inferiority. He would put in his time, as he had done in so many other programs, to make Mom happy. He knew the routine.

But Teen Challenge wasn't like any other program he attended. The other programs taught about taking control, being the master of your own destiny, managing your mind, and self-control—all on your own strength. Teen Challenge taught him that he could do none of those things without the Lord, but that with the Lord nothing was impossible[xviii]—even deliverance from drugs and addiction.

Dad said a member of the program staff told him to look in a mirror. "See the guy in the mirror? He's the problem—not your mother or father or wife. You." He then added, "But there's a solution for your problem: a man named Jesus."

Dad learned about accountability and restoration. He learned that the Lord didn't want to just heal him; He wanted to restore him and give him life, abundant life.[xix] Most important, Dad learned that he could come to know Jesus intimately, the Son of the living God.

Through the ministry of Teen Challenge Dad made Jesus his personal Lord and Savior. Mom accepted Christ not long after. Both were convinced there was no other way to live.

Dad left everything to follow Christ, including his business and his friends. Discerning that the Lord was calling him into ministry, he started working part time at the church he and Mom began attending, serving under the direction of the senior pastor. He grew in his relationship with Christ and, after a year of faithful service to the Lord, at the pastor's urging, he agreed to take on the youth ministry.

Though my dad did not have a college education or pastoral degree, was not eloquent or masterful, the Lord called him into the ministry. His first commission resulted in a lifetime of Christian service. He went from being youth pastor to assistant pastor to senior pastor.

"Today," Dad would say whenever he testified, "I can't imagine anything more rewarding than serving my Savior. Drug addict turned pastor—only the goodness of the Lord could have shaped such a miracle."

I TOOK THE LONG WAY HOME

As a child, I heard both Mom and Dad's testimony of salvation. Dad's was vivid with detail and tattooed to my heart. Because of his drastic transformation, he was asked to testify frequently at churches, conventions, reunions. I'd heard it my whole life—publicly and intimately. It was part of us. My dad: reformed drug addict. Now pastor.

Mom's testimony was more elusive. It had been years since I'd heard it. So when the opportunity arose for Mom to share— only about six months prior to my own revelation—she didn't hesitate to call me. She and Dad had just begun pastoring at a new church and, expectedly, as the pastor's wife, and also an ordained minister, she was asked to share her testimony.

"Mark your calendar," she told me. "I'm speaking at our women's fellowship service. June 11th. It's a Friday." She spoke in a forceful tone that forbade my refusal. I didn't question. I simply marked my calendar. Despite my spiritual status, I knew I had to be there to support my mother.

When June 11th arrived, I dressed nicely, and Domenic and I traveled to Mom and Dad's new church. It was a two hour drive with traffic but I didn't mind. I knew it meant a lot to her that I attend.

I dropped Domenic off at my parents' house so he could spend time with Dad and arrived for the Friday evening service just a few minutes before it started.

Though I strategically arrived late to avoid Mom's notoriously embarrassing introductions, she managed to seize me at the door just in time to introduce me to Sister Rebecca, the leader of the annual fellowship, a tall African American woman, with shoulder length hair, hazel eyes, and bright red lips.

"This is my daughter, Stephanie," Mom said.

"Hi, Stephanie." Rebecca reached out to hug me, her floral perfume enveloping me. "What a lovely young woman you are. Praise the Lord!"

Before I could even utter a thank you, Mom graciously informed her that I was not living for the Lord. "You really need to keep her in prayer," she said.

I shuddered at Mom's candidness. Surely she wasn't telling a perfect stranger that I had only come to the fellowship out of obligation.

"She loved Jesus as a child, but when those teenage years came around, she went into the world and never came back."

She really was, I thought. If I didn't love her so much I would have choked her.

"But I have no doubt that someday she'll give her life back to Jesus," Mom assured. "She'll surrender all. He promised me."

"Absolutely no doubt," Rebecca replied. And then, placing her arm around me, she asked if she could pray with me. I couldn't refuse.

She led the three of us in a short, powerful prayer that ignited several, "Yes, Lords," from my mother.

As she closed with a solid *amen,* Sister Rebecca looked at me and said which I presumed she intended as prophetic, "You'll be sharing your testimony someday."

"Maybe," I responded smugly, wanting really to say, "I don't think so." But instead, I thanked her for her prayer and then excused myself into the sanctuary, from which I could already hear the blend of warm-up music: piano, drums, and guitar.

Mom soon joined me inside, directing me to move to the front row. We arrived in our seats just as the service officially began with prayer.

A redheaded young woman, with porcelain white skin and green eyes, gifted in song and piano playing, then led the roomful of women in none other than *"I Surrender All,"* a hymn that I knew by heart and to which I couldn't help but sing along. I could only assume that somehow in the thirty seconds it took me to find my seat that sister Rebecca requested the song just for me.

As I stood beside Mom, my soft voice droned out by the intensity of hers, I stifled a laugh as she belted out the last few words of the first verse and moved closer to the chorus, digging into the song with passion, "I surrender all...all to Jesus..." Her voice was noticeably louder than any other woman in our row and showed no sign of softening. Glancing at her, I remembered what she told me when I was a teenager when I questioned why she sang so loudly. "I'm singing to my Savior," she told me. "And that's not something I'll quiet down for." With eyes shut and both hands raised, she was indeed worshiping her Redeemer.

Sister Rebecca introduced my mother after the song service. "I'd now like to introduce our pastor's wife, Reverend Angela Cavelli."

Mom marched up on stage with her Bible and a stack of note cards. "God is good," she shouted into the podium microphone.

The women's response was unanimous: "All the time!"

Mom opened with prayer and then shared a brief introduction before delving headfirst into her testimony.

"How many of you here today were born in religious homes?" Mom asked the women in the sanctuary.

"Now, I'm not talking about homes where your parents had relationships with God, I'm talking religion. Rituals. Traditions. Anyone here raised very religious?" From my peripheral vision, I saw hands raised throughout the sanctuary in response.

"Good. Then most of you will relate." Mom walked down from the platform and into the aisle. "My parents were very religious people. I was born and raised Catholic and went to Catholic school for thirteen years." She placed her hand on her hip. "But I'll be honest, I never really knew a thing about God. Not like I do now. I knew a lot about religion but nothing about a Savior."

"See, no one ever told me that I could know Jesus personally. I had no idea that I could tell Him everything, that He could be my best friend like He is now." Mom strode back and forth, from one end of the aisle to the other, talking about her life as a child and then into adulthood—how she had lived life without her best friend.

"I had no clue that I needed God," she admitted. "I thought if I got married, it would help and I'd be happy. Then I figured maybe if I had some babies that would make things better. Then maybe if I made some money. It just went on and on. But it wasn't until I found Jesus that I was truly happy and really found peace."

"When I started going to the church my husband and I attended when we were first saved, I thought the people were a little crazy. The singing. Clapping. Raising the hands." Responding to the audience's laughter, Mom added, "I thought it was some sort of a cult. But I was so drawn to whatever it was that made those people sing and clap and raise their hands."

"My husband wanted it too. He wasn't the pastor you all know today. He was on drugs then, but he knew the Answer was in whatever those people were singing about."

I heard a woman behind me gasp when Mom shared about Dad's drug addition. I could relate. Sometimes it was hard for me to believe.

I never knew the man Dad used to be. I only knew the saved man, the pastor. If it wasn't for the pictures of Dad's emaciated physique stashed in boxes in the corner of my parents' attic, I'd have thought his story was a hoax. *My dad? On drugs?* Not the guy who had us at church three times a week. The man who forbade secular music in our house. The man who sang hymns in the mall. The man who volunteered to drive a busload of senior citizens to Lancaster, Pennsylvania every month for luncheons and shopping. There must be some mistake. But the pictures were indisputable evidence.

"My husband's salvation was instant," Mom continued. "I took a little longer because I didn't think anything was wrong with me. I was a good person. I went to work, raised my babies, cooked and cleaned. I didn't see any need to turn my life over to the Lord. I felt like the victim in our marriage. I prayed for God to change my husband. But God said to me, 'You need to look at yourself.' I was shocked! *Me? What was wrong with me?* That's when God started showing me my faults. And there were many!"

"It wasn't until I repented of my sins and asked Jesus into my heart, that I was at peace for the first time in my life."

I sat in the front row, smiling inside. Though it had been years since I heard it, Mom's testimony remained the same. I couldn't relate to her transformation, but it was nice to hear something genuine in a world of insincerity.

The service ended with an altar call. But I slipped out early, careful to avoid any more unexpected prayers from strangers.

Mom met me back at the house for dessert while Dad and Domenic attended a men's Bible study.

"Why didn't you stay for the altar call?" she asked me, entering the house.

"I was afraid you'd broadcast my alleged rebellion to the whole congregation."

"I wouldn't do that."

"Didn't want to chance it." I stood at the stove beside a pot of water I began heating for tea.

"Sit," my mother commanded, reaching for the pot handle. "I'll do this. You get the ice cream."

"Ma," I said as I retrieved the chocolate ice cream from the freezer, not considering the potential outcome of the question, "You really didn't know anything about God while growing up?"

"Not a thing," she said, turning the burner up. "I was so lost. I wish my parents raised me the way Dad and I raised you." She shook her head. "You don't know the value of your upbringing."

"Yes I do."

"No. You don't know the worth of Jesus."

"Just because I'm not a diehard Christian like you and Dad doesn't mean I don't know Jesus."

"You wouldn't look so miserable if you knew Jesus."

"I'm not miserable," I scolded, scooping the ice cream into a bowl. "I have a wonderful son. Great boyfriend. And I'm hugely successful. Why would I be miserable?"

"You have everything you thought would make you happy, but are you at peace with yourself?"

"Yes," I answered, starting to bubble inside like the water on the stove.

"Are you disappointed with life?"

"What?"

"You don't have to answer. Your eyes tell me you are."

"I'm not disappointed with anything," I scoffed.

"Oh, okay," she uttered as if it was news to her.

Turning the burner off, she poured the boiling water into two mugs. Then, bringing the mugs to the table, she set one beside my ice cream bowl.

"Do you know who holds your future, Steph?"

"I really don't want to talk about this, Ma—" I tried to interrupt her but she continued in spite of me.

"If you die tonight, do you know where you'll spend eternity?" she asked, stirring her tea. "*I do*, without a shadow of a doubt. I'd rather have that assurance than all the money and success in the world."

I sat quietly as Mom rambled on, nodding in amusement between mouthfuls of ice cream, but soaking in her words in spite of myself. She used every chance she had to tell me about the Lord. He was her treasure, her best friend, and she couldn't fathom the reasons I didn't want to know Him.

Straining her teabag, she went on, though I wished she would stop, "I can't wait for the day when we'll all sit around this dinner table and talk about our love for Christ. It's coming soon. A lot of prayers went into you kids. Your brother, too. I know he's a sinner," she said as if it was something I didn't know. "But I guess you both will have to find the Lord for yourselves."

Dad and Domenic moseyed in from Bible study, halting our conversation.

"Hey, where's my ice cream?" Domenic kidded.

"I'll get it for you." Mom jumped from her seat.

"How was the service?" Dad asked.

"Testimony's still in tact," I said.

"Glory to God," he replied. "Only by His grace are we here today. Right, Steph?"

"Sure." I swallowed a spoonful of chocolate.

"You guys sleeping over?" Dad asked.

"Can we, Mom, can we?" Domenic pleaded. "Pop said we can help clean out the attic tomorrow."

"The stuff up there really needs to be organized," Mom informed.

"If you really need us," I yielded as Domenic excitedly jumped in the air. *Anything to help Mom and Dad.*

The next morning, just as promised, Domenic and I rose early to clean the attic.

But I began to regret the promise the minute I pulled down the ladder from the ceiling and climbed into the musty space that extended at least fifty feet in every direction. Our job was to organize everything: rummage through all the dusty boxes and trash bags and make three piles: save, give away, and junk. The problem was neither Domenic nor I knew which should go into each pile. And organization was not my forte.

Looking across the sea of plastic and cardboard, everything looked like junk to me—all but one corner of the attic, where my great-grandmother's cedar chest sat. My eyes brightened at the sight of it. I would've recognized that chest anywhere, and I knew exactly what it held: old photos of Mom and Dad—their "before-Jesus albums."

I scaled the puffy trash bags that blocked my path until I made it to Grandma's chest. "You need to see this," I told Domenic, who idled by the entrance. I cracked open the heavy lid, which instantly released the stench of mothballs and cedar.

Domenic didn't try to climb over the bags toward me; instead he jumped over them like a football player diving for a touchdown. He flipped from one to the next, then tumbled to his feet, all while making combat noises as if he were involved in some imaginary battle. That boy could find fun in everything.

By the time he made it to me, I'd pulled out a bundle of crinkled three-by-four-inch photos from the '70s—with white borders and dates printed on the sides. The first few I found were of Dad, dated 1974. I grimaced. The man in the photos was ugly: tall and gangly, with long, oily blonde hair that was parted in the middle and straggled lifelessly past his shoulders. His gray skin was covered with acne and stubble. He wore a silk shirt and tight jeans, thick leather belt, and four-inch platform shoes. With a cigarette wedged behind his ear, and another dangling from his mouth, he was the quintessential bad boy—the world's idea of a good time.

"Recognize this guy?" I asked Domenic as he leaned his head on my shoulder.

"Should I?" he asked.

"It's Pop."

"No way!" he shrieked, snatching the picture from me and examining it closely. "Pop smoked?" he asked, eyes bulging.

"Like a chimney."

"Was this before he was a Christian?"

"Of course," I said. "Long before."

We flipped through a few more stained and wrinkled photos of Dad before stumbling upon one of Mom. She was beautiful. Thin and shapely, with long, wavy auburn hair, flawless tanned skin, and liquid blue eyes. She was 100 percent Italian: half Calabrese and half Sicilian. Domenic could scarcely believe it was his grandmother. "She looks so...different." He scrunched his face in disbelief, shocked that the woman he knew as Mom-mom could ever have been so young and stunning.

Mom came up to join us, breathing heavily. "Oh, dear," she said when she saw us practically buried behind the piles of bags and boxes. "Look at this mess. You guys will be here for hours. I'd better think about what we'll have for dinner."

Dad grunted up each step of the ladder as if he were strapped with hundred-pound weights, sighing and calling for the help of the Lord. When he finally made it up, he asked, "Where in the world did all this stuff come from?"

"Hey, Pop," Domenic called, from across the room "come see these pictures we found!"

My parents exchanged a look, their eyes telling each other they'd rather avoid looking at those old photos. But because it was Domenic asking, they would ignite the nostalgia they had worked so hard to renounce.

By the time Mom and Dad made it over to us, lifting bags and sliding boxes out of their way, and settled on the floor beside us, we'd come upon their wedding album. Domenic laughed at his grandfather's bow tie and platform shoes. "What were you thinking, Pop," he asked, "wearing those high heels?"

"That was the style back then," Dad said, sliding the album onto his lap. "Wasn't your Mom-mom a knockout?"

Domenic nodded.

Mom certainly was a beauty, but Dad was like the beast. He looked as if he'd crawled out of bed and hopped into a tuxedo seconds before the camera snapped. His hair was unkempt and unwashed, and his expression morbid, as if someone had forced him there at gunpoint.

Mom laughed. "Pop looked so bad that day, the photographer refused to take any pictures of him. He sent him home and told him not to come back until his hair was combed and washed. Pop left, but when he came back he almost looked worse."

"Well, at least I know you didn't marry me just for my looks," Dad said, laughing at his own joke.

I loved poring over the old photos of Mom and Dad. It was like entering a world unknown to me, looking at strangers. I never knew the people in the pictures, nor will I ever. They were like a mirage. "What happened to you?" I asked.

"Jesus happened to us," Mom said.

It seemed unreal, part of some conspiracy. But it was all documented in those photos. The camera had immortalized them, but the Lord had restored them.

5 Growing up with Jesus

Mom and Dad's love for Jesus was woven into every facet of our lives while growing up. He was truly the center of our world. But having Jesus as our center, our High Priest, made us very different, separate from our non-believing neighbors and relatives and, almost always, I felt like we were the *outsiders*.

One major difference was that we were one of the few families in the neighborhood that wasn't Catholic. For many years, we were the only non-Catholics amongst our extended family. Mom and Dad left Catholicism once they asked Jesus into their hearts and became born again Protestants. They embraced the Word of God and the teachings of Jesus, which were taught openly in the church they joined.

It wasn't a surprise to Mom or Dad when their families disapproved of their conversion. Mom's mother opposed it adamantly, acting as if they'd burn in hell for all eternity if they didn't belong to the Catholic Church. Grandma Pinto was nearly hospitalized when Mom informed her that neither my brother nor I would go to Catholic school or participate in the traditional rituals. To her, not being Catholic was unlawful. But to Mom, Catholic and Protestant were just labels that had little significance to her eternal destination. It was the change in her heart that mattered.

Dad's parents didn't know what to think. As far as they knew, Italians were Catholic. Period. Mom and Dad's conversion confused them. But whatever Protestantism taught seemed to work for Dad. Considering he'd nearly succumbed to his addiction numerous times and both Grandma and Grandpa had considered him dead, they welcomed Dad's salvation. This Jesus Dad had found did what no psychologist, psychiatrist, counselor, or rehabilitation center could do. Christ had saved their son, giving him a new life, and both Grandma and Grandpa Cavelli were grateful. If detaching from the Catholic Church was the most they had to worry about, they felt fortunate.

Mom and Dad didn't care what anyone thought. They'd found the Truth, and the Truth had set them free from religion and condemnation.[xx] They made Jesus the center of their lives and ours. Everything else came second.

They had us kids in church whenever the doors were open—morning, noon, or night. Nothing stopped them. Not the mountains of snow that piled up in winter around our small Dodge hatchback or the torrential downpours of spring and fall that flooded our basement and knocked out the electricity. Whatever the cost, whether on the bus or by foot, Mom and Dad found a way to get us to church.

The neighbors thought we were crazy. I remember ducking away from my parents as they walked down our narrow street on many warm summer nights, when our neighbors sat outside their tenement-style row houses on beach chairs with music blasting from their windows. My brother and I would either run ahead or lag behind, watching our parents from a distance, embarrassed by the dictionary-sized Bibles they proudly carried as they glided past the ogling neighbors. We hoped no one would notice the familial connection. But the neighbors all waved and smiled, offering their "hellos" and "God bless yous" as they whispered among themselves, eyeing the pastor and his wife. "I could never practice their religion," one would sneer. "They're at church every day!"

Having a father who was a pastor was another factor that made us different. The other neighborhood kids' had fathers with normal professions like carpenters and electricians and mailmen. Most of them didn't even know what a pastor was. "How can your father be married if he's a priest?" they'd ask.

"He's not a priest," I explained. "He's a pastor."

They'd just look at me, wide-eyed and dumbfounded, and shrug as if *pastor* was a foreign word. In many ways we were foreigners. Mom said we were in this world but not of it.[xxi] "We're a peculiar people, Stephanie" she'd tell me, "a chosen generation."[xxii] It wasn't until many years later that I would understand just how foreign we were.

My parents' choice of schooling for me and my brother also contributed to our separation from the rest of the world. Instead of going to public or parochial grammar school like the other neighborhood kids, we attended our church's Christian academy, where my father served in several capacities, including bus driver and school administrator. The church/school was my second home.

I TOOK THE LONG WAY HOME

If I hadn't gone to school with a handful of other kids who also took up a secondary residence in the church/school, I'd have thought these things were too weird. But thankfully I had the "regulars"—that's what us church-going kids called ourselves. We were the children who attended every Sunday church service, Wednesday prayer meeting, and Friday night Bible study. *Regularly.* Our parents just couldn't get enough.

Many of our parents were not raised as Christians. Like my mom and dad, they'd found Jesus at some point in their lives when they had exhausted every other option. Some of them were recovering drug addicts or alcoholics, others were teachers or accountants or business owners—each with a remarkable story of how God transformed his or her life into something special and wonderful. He'd given them beauty for ashes,[xxiii] exchanged their past lives for something new.

Church was their meeting place, their rest and safety from the outside world. There they would sing hymns together, study passages of Scripture, and unite in prayer. In every way we were a family united by Christ and had everything in common.[xxiv] Regardless of background or race or level of education we were all part of the invisible body of Christ.

Despite my similarities with the other regulars, there was one event that Dad and Mom engaged us in that I was certain didn't occur in any other home on the planet: daily family devotions.

Promptly at seven o'clock every night, Dad would call my brother and me to the living room for our family's prayer and worship time. It seemed as if the moment Michael and I were having the most fun, Dad's spiritual alarm clock went off. "Steph, Michael, let's go. Time for devotions," he would say excitedly, as if he couldn't wait to share the Word with us.

Michael and I never shared his enthusiasm. We'd trudge down the stairs and plop on our velvet, floral-print couch like rag dolls. I'd let out a long sigh of boredom and shoot a look Michael's way that said, *If only our parents were normal.*

Dad and Mom sat on either side of us. Dad would flip through the Bible while Mom searched for a hymn. Once we were settled, Mom would pass out our hymnbooks and announce the page number. "*'All that Thrills My Soul Is Jesus,'* page 235," she'd say. Our hymnbooks were old and tattered, leftovers from when our church purchased new books. We were privileged to have six: four for the family and two extra for guests.

Dad would open with a short prayer, then lead us in song. He'd move his arm like a music conductor—up, down, back and forth—making his best effort to get us singing in unison and on key. None of us could carry a note. Dad's singing voice sounded like a flooded car engine, while Mom's sounded like a high-pitched squawk that cracked as each note fluctuated. But they sang with all their hearts, louder with each verse. I wondered if they realized that the walls of our row home were paper thin.

After our mini song service was over, Dad would read Scripture and then review what he'd read. He tried all kinds of things to get us excited about devotions. Sometimes he interjected a Bible trivia game or a "sword fight" between my brother, Mom, and me—the sword, of course, being the Bible. Dad would call out a Scripture verse, and the first of us to find it would win the round. Mom or I usually won, with my brother always lagging behind. Whenever we sensed Michael growing frustrated, pouting, and close to tears, Mom and I would exchange a look or a wink, then let him win the next round. That one win would set him ablaze with confidence. You'd think the kid had won an Oscar.

Dad also initiated a time for us to give thanks. He wanted us to know how blessed we were as Christians, and always encouraged us to give God praise during devotions. We each had to take a turn listing five things for which we were thankful—and we couldn't repeat. If we thanked the Lord for the sun and stars the night before, Dad would encourage us to think of something else. "There's so much to be thankful for," he'd say when either of us shrugged or said we couldn't think of anything. Eventually, something always came to mind.

I always looked forward to hearing Michael's top five. With a serious, sincere expression, he'd thank God for his shoelaces, for tissues—"because without them we'd have to blow our noses on our sleeves!"—or for Mom's pork chops. Dad often broke his own rule by thanking the Lord for Mom. "I thank the Lord for giving me a precious rose from his garden," he'd say, gazing at her. She'd smirk in embarrassment, sometimes roll her eyes, but then give him a look of love and gratitude. She never said it, but we all knew she was thankful for Dad. There was warmth and sensitivity between them, a deep respect that to this day they attribute only to the grace of God.

Prayer was the most difficult part of the whole experience.

I TOOK THE LONG WAY HOME

I could have easily managed the whole thing as an only child, but there was something about my younger brother's animated reactions that always forced me to start trouble.

My brother was a quiet kid, but extremely silly. Dad scolded him regularly in church for outbursts of laughter. He'd laugh at anything. All you had to do was cross your eyes; he'd be rolling on the floor. Mention the word *fart*, and the kid would go into cardiac arrest. He was so ticklish that if my forefinger was in close proximity to his stomach or waist—not even touching him—he'd be wetting his pants in an explosion of laughter. He had an infectious laugh, like Porky Pig's. His face would redden like an apple and his cheeks inflated like a balloon. A thick dimple emerged just beneath his right eye. You'd think he was choking.

After our time of sharing thanks and prayer requests, the four of us would kneel at the couch to pray. Michael always started since he was the youngest. On most occasions his prayer was predictable. "Dear God, thank You for this day, thank You for all that You've given us, thank You for making me, thank You for my family. Please help all the homeless people, and help me too. Amen."

Following Michael's prayer was mine, then Mom's, and last Dad's. The trouble didn't start until midway through Mom's prayer, which was usually the longest. My mind would wander while she prayed, then I'd realize that I had a prime source of entertainment kneeling right beside me: my silly little brother. I'd nudge his arm with my elbow. His head would pop up from the couch cushion like a jack-in-the-box—big, cheesy grin already planted on his face as if he'd been sitting in wait for my summons. We'd do what we could to entertain ourselves in silence during the remainder of our prayer time. We made faces at each other or tried to guess what the other was saying while moving our mouths. We did this for as long as we could, as quietly as we could, with Mom and Dad kneeling beside us in prayer, until a giggle would seep through one of our mouths. Instantly we'd thrust our heads down into the couch cushion and remain like statues in hopes that Mom and Dad hadn't heard the laugh that escaped. Mom would stop in mid-sentence, pause, then continue. The silence was an unspoken warning that we'd better behave. Our heads would remain frozen in those cushions until Dad began to pray.

There was then a new dilemma: whether to continue our silly behavior and provoke a forthcoming spanking, or bite the bullet and stay still for a few more minutes.

It was a tough decision, but occasionally, we decided that whatever consequence lay ahead was worth it.

While my brother's head was down in the cushion, I'd pose my face in a crooked, wild gesture, waiting for him to catch a glimpse. Just one look through his peripheral vision was sure to invoke an eruption of laughter. Sure enough, his little eyeballs peeked out from his folded arms, and the expression on my face incited a quick burst of spitting laughter.

It simultaneously incited some swift action from Dad, who had no tolerance for disruptions during prayer—especially while he was praying. He leaped from his position, grabbed my brother by the arm, and spanked his butt three times—pow, crack, boom! I plunged my head in the couch cushion in an attempt to prove my innocence, hoping Dad's large, swift hand would skip right over my bottom. But Dad was no fool. He knew Michael had an accomplice, so I caught the tail end of Dad's wrath—pow, crack, boom!—before he caved back into position and finished his prayer.

Michael and I sat silently for a few seconds, our bottoms red and throbbing.

Then I looked at my brother and exchanged one last smirk.

6 True Christians

Whenever I think of people who genuinely loved Christ as much as my parents did I can't help but think of some of the men in the church I attended while growing up.

Some were born and raised in the church and never entered the world. Their lives reflected a standard of holiness that always amazed me: how God had carried them through their walks with Him, from adolescences to adulthood. They led their wives and children, serving as the spiritual leader and high priest. They loved Jesus for a lifetime. Their gentle, humble spirits were so inspiring. They were the Daniels and Josephs of our church. Consistent in their walk. Faithful and true. They stored up for themselves treasures in heaven.[xxv] Some of them, no doubt, when they went to their real Home, gained eternal rewards and are now awaiting the arrival of their brothers and sisters as we continue to run the race. They were genuine men of God.

The most memorable of all these men were the handful of Teen Challenge graduates who, like Dad, had made our church their home. Some led church services at prisons or hospitals, others held prayer meetings in their homes or businesses, but all had testimonies of how God's grace had restored their lives. They didn't speak eloquently; they weren't educated or well mannered; they were just men with hearts after God's own. Mom called them the Peters and Pauls of modern day. I called them *true Christians*.

Jimmy, a short, stocky Italian, was the Peter of the group, the impetuous rock who'd cut off a man's ear for his Lord. He grew up on the streets of Philadelphia and was known as a fighter. Prior to knowing Jesus, he was a drug addict. A husband and father of three daughters, he would leave his house to buy a quart of milk from the corner store and not return for weeks. Someone would see him wandering the neighborhood, talking about spaceships and aliens. He looked like a homeless person, lost and destitute. He was a menace. A waste of life.

But Jesus saw something special in Jimmy. He saw a life worth saving. In 1980, after being thrown out of his home, with nowhere to go and no one to turn to, he entered Teen Challenge.

There he learned about restoration, about a grace that surpassed any remedy the world could concoct.

Most guys needed one year in Teen Challenge, some two; Jimmy needed three. But during those years the Lord touched him in a deep way. He became addicted to the ultimate remedy: the King of kings and Lord of lords. His sins were cleansed, washed away in the deepest ocean. But even better, he was granted the gift of salvation—a gift that would guarantee his eternal destiny. Jimmy was born again, given a heart transplant, with Christ as his surgeon.

Once Jimmy graduated from Teen Challenge, he immediately began serving the Lord. God worked through him to minister to men in some of the worst prisons in Philadelphia. One Sunday each month, Jimmy took a van of Christian brothers to the state penitentiary, where he conducted church services for the inmates. Month after month, he testified about men who came to know Jesus in a personal way as a result of his ministry.

Jimmy was instrumental in getting many brothers into Teen Challenge and following up with them after graduation. Jimmy had his own unique way of ministering to the men. I witnessed a few encounters from afar.

One Wednesday night service in particular sticks out in my mind. It was a cold and damp, mid-March service. The sanctuary was filled with quiet laughter and the hum of voices. A few minutes before service began, a recent Teen Challenge grad strolled in. The man was over six feet tall, brawny, and wore an oversized sweatshirt and sweatpants. His hair was jelled neatly in place; his rounded face donned tinted glasses. Jimmy spotted the man the moment he entered the room. "Yo, Joe," he said in his gruff, serious voice. He walked toward the man, who stood frozen at the sound of Jimmy's powerful voice—like a kid caught stealing. "Where were you on Sunday?" Jimmy asked, closing in on Joe until they stood face to face.

Joe stammered and shrugged, gathering words that came out almost against his will. "I, uh, was at my sister's."

Recognizing an insufficient excuse, Jimmy shook his head. "You make it your business to be here on Sundays. No excuses. I don't care what you gotta do. You got that?"

Joe nodded.

"I mean it, brother. I'll be looking for you. And if I don't find you, I'll come get you. And you don't want that."

Joe promised to be in church.

I never understood how these huge men, noticeably larger than Jimmy, would let him bark orders. The explanation was simple. They knew he loved them.

Jimmy ministered to the men no one else wanted. He would literally take them off the streets, out of halfway houses and from under cardboard blankets in the parks, and get them into Teen Challenge. He knew how to reach them through tough love. "Don't even try to leave the program," he'd threaten, shaking his large clenched fist. "Because if you do, I'll hunt you down, and trust me, you'll wish you never left." This was Jimmy's way of saying, "I really care."

Jimmy didn't have a college degree, a big house, or a fancy car. But God doesn't look at the outside appearance, as man does; He looks at the heart.xxvi And in Jimmy's heart, He saw kindness and compassion. He saw availability. He saw a man who, more than two decades after his salvation, was still brimming with love, a man who couldn't contain the abundant life God had given him. A man with the looks of a street thug who told everyone he met about Jesus: the gas attendant, the cashier, the doctor, the policeman. "Yo, buddy," he'd say. "You know Jesus loves you?"

Ted was another one. Drug addict and convicted thief, he had been on trial for murder at the age of eighteen. He didn't actually commit the crime, but he was there, an accomplice. By the grace of God, a compassionate Philadelphia judge ordered him to go to Teen Challenge. And there, like Jimmy and my dad, he accepted Jesus as his Savior and never looked back.

Ted was the stepfather of one of my closest friends while growing up. Lee and her family lived two streets away from us. She was one of us regulars. We went to school, church, Sunday school, Missionettes, and Bible studies together.

Lee was like a bull, athletic and strong. She was the sister I never had, my dependable playmate. When we weren't in church, we rode our bikes around the neighborhood or played games. I don't think a day passed between the ages of eight and thirteen that I didn't see her. The two of us were inseparable.

Tomboys, with straggly hair and street clothes, we played football and wall ball, competed with boys at skateboarding and running. We scurried through the streets like two unleashed dogs who'd escaped confinement—wild and untamed.

Occasionally, we settled for indoor games. Lee's house— always the preferred venue—was our primary destination. It had central air conditioning, which was rare for an aged Philadelphia row home, not to mention the generous selection of board games and video games she had accumulated as an only child. Our only obstacle was her mother.

She was a petite, feisty Italian woman, pretty and well tanned all year round, with reddish-blonde streaked hair that fell just below her shoulders. Her face was always made up to perfection, no matter what time of day. Lee and I were both a full head taller than her, but she had us in check nonetheless. If we decided to play in her house, she'd run down the rules before we made it through the vestibule, waving her finger in our faces in a threatening tone that commanded obedience. *No screaming, no wrestling, and absolutely no fighting.* "Let me tell ya sumthin'," she'd say in her south Philly accent. "If I hear youse fightin' up 'ere, I'm killin' youse both. Got it?" We nodded: *we got it.*

But nothing seemed to keep us from fighting. It was part of our friendship. We just learned to keep it quiet. We'd break out in major battles in Lee's bedroom over whether or not a word was eligible in our Scrabble tournaments. Faces would burn in anger, sarcastic remarks were exchanged, a nudge here and a poke there would quickly escalate to a fierce shove and punch, until fists would fly and heads would lock. Lee attacked first, her thick body jolting upward and then crashing on top of my scrawny frame like a hundred-pound punching bag. I came back with swift, sharp kicks to her thighs and chest, high strikes to the face and neck, fingernails digging into skin. Eventually we became a ball of arms and legs, tangled hair and twisted feet, circling her bed in a fierce struggle for victory. It would carry on in silence, barring the occasional grunt and thump, until one of us knocked into a dresser or banged into the wall. Then we heard Lee's mom scream from wherever she was in the house, "Lee!" Her voice shrieked through half the neighborhood. "Youse better not be fightin' up 'ere!" We instantly broke apart.

Dusting ourselves off, we exchanged a look of death, and carried on with our game of Scrabble as if nothing had happened. Lee was the only girl with whom I could share laughs, dreams, and punches—all in the same day.

Lee had a natural beauty about her that set her apart from most people. Her smile lit up a room, with bright white teeth and cherry red lips. Her hair was the color of mahogany, poker straight, and too thick and straight to even braid. Her skin was tan, her eyes a deep brown. I doubt she had any clue how pretty she was. If she did realize, it didn't faze her. She had more important things to think about.

While many of us regulars wanted little to do with the Lord, Lee couldn't get enough. She soaked Him up like a sponge, absorbing all the knowledge and understanding she could. Nothing could keep her quiet about her Lord. She told everyone about Christ and didn't care what anyone said about her or to her. She told our classmates in fifth and sixth grade that the Lord would "spit them out of His mouth"[xxvii] if they didn't repent of their sins. She was our very own John the Baptist.

Lee was like the seed sown on good soil. She heard the Word, accepted it, and produced a crop—thirty, sixty, or even a hundred times what was sown. I was like the seed sown among thorns. When the worries of life and the deceitfulness of wealth and the desires for other things came along, they choked the Word that had been planted in me.[xxviii] We both heard the same Word. We were both placed on the same path. But she traveled on and I veered off in my own direction.

As we moved on to high school and into college, we grew apart. Lee followed the Lord; I followed the world. She went to Bible College to become a missionary, while I went to a secular school. I chose the broader way, and Lee chose the narrow, less traveled path toward Christ.

We kept in touch through letters and phone calls. She'd write about the wonderful things the Lord was doing in her life and how He continued to open many doors for her. Her letters always sounded positive and joyful. I often wondered, whenever I wrote back, what my life would be like if I'd joined Lee in choosing Jesus.

Lee and I were brought back together in our junior year of college when she was diagnosed with leukemia. I saw her three times throughout that year: once in the hospital when her legs were swollen like tree stumps and she was barely recognizable, and once in her home when the cancer was in remission. The last time I saw her on earth was in a casket at our home church in Philadelphia. Lee went home to be with Jesus at the age of twenty-one, less than two years after diagnosis.

Hospital workers knew her as the boisterous Italian girl who told them all about Jesus. Lee capitalized on every opportunity to proclaim the love of Christ—even in a hospital bed. Nothing could separate her from this great love she'd found in Him. Neither death nor life, neither angels nor demons, neither the present nor the future, nor any powers, neither height nor depth, nor anything else in all creation could separate her from the love she found in Jesus.[xxix] She didn't have any problems or addictions, no terrible childhood from which she was running; she just loved Jesus. And Lee is now with her Savior.

Dad and his friends found that same love. They knew Lee's Jesus. And like Lee, they couldn't help but tell the world.

Dad, Jimmy, Ted, and several other men with similar stories would pile into the church van with boxes of Christian literature on Saturdays and head out to the most derelict places in Philadelphia in hopes of sharing the great message of salvation. On the way they took turns telling jokes, with *Amens* and *Thank You, Lords* shouted intermittently. They sang choruses; among the favorites was "I Have Decided to Follow Jesus." Like baseball players singing the national anthem, they sang with all their hearts, their voices blended in seamless unison, a low alto pitch reverberating throughout the van. But theirs was a much greater anthem.

I have decided to follow Jesus,
No turning back, no turning back.
Though none go with me, still I will follow.
No turning back, no turning back.[xxx]

There was no turning back for any of them. They'd found the greatest gift of all. It wasn't wealth or prestige, drugs or alcohol—not even the families with which they were blessed; it was in Jesus, His love, His favor. There was no rest for them in the world, as man will never find his rest until he finds it in God.[xxxi] They journeyed toward the prize, their eyes fixed on the Savior. They invested in eternal rewards, things that could never be lost, stolen, or broken.

I never understood what drove them. They clapped the hardest, sang the loudest, prayed the longest, attended the most services. Most of them bore physical evidence of their former lives: scars, tattoos, missing fingers; but all were transformed into new creatures. Whenever Pastor asked for testimonies, they were the first to jump to their feet. I didn't understand until years later that their joy came from being forgiven. They were acquitted by grace and renewed through faith. Their sins were permanently submerged in God's sea of forgetfulness, and they couldn't keep their love and gratitude contained.

Their lives were proof that God works through the murderer, the drug addict, the thief, the uneducated, the illiterate,

I TOOK THE LONG WAY HOME

the drunk, the failure. He chooses the foolish things of the world to shame the wise, the weak and lowly and despised things of the world to shame the strong.[xxxii] Indeed, He uses our flaws and our wretchedness for His glory. We've all sinned and fallen short of the glory of God[xxxiii]—every last one of us. But God loves the sinner. He pursues us with an unrelenting pursuit until we yield, until we realize that Jesus is indeed the Answer. No matter what we've done or who we have sinned against, God's infinite love is capable of forgiving us. Again and again. And those who are forgiven much love much.[xxxiv]

Ironically, I was just as lost as Dad and his friends. With my education and my great-paying job, I was empty. Instead of drugs, I was addicted to money and success and possessions. I worshiped me. But underneath it all, I had no peace. My heart was so littered with debris there was no room for Christ. I filled it with imitations to keep me temporarily satisfied. I went from one project to the next, one interest to the next, in pursuit of *something*, but I was always left half full.

I knew the peace I needed was out there, a fulfillment that money couldn't buy and man could never manufacture. I just hadn't accepted it yet.

7 First Love

My story is much different from Mom and Dad's and the Teen Challenge graduates I admired so much as a child.

I had the quintessential Christian upbringing, the kind after which Christian parents try to model.

Because my parents were first-generation Protestants, they wanted to ensure their rearing was totally biblical. In doing so, they assumed it was their duty to impart on us kids the rules for a healthy Christian lifestyle: the rules according to an ultraconservative Pentecostal church. Hence, there was no secular music in our house, no cable television, no dancing, no alcohol, no movies, no designer clothes or sneakers. Anything that was even remotely considered worldly was forbidden in our household. Mom and Dad believed that if we were to be Christians, we were to be set apart from the world, in it but certainly not of it.[xxxv]

But all those rules were the least of my worries. What was more disconcerting was Dad's conviction about dating: specifically, there would be none until I entered college. Good old Dad had practically mapped out my life. I would attend a Christian Bible school, where I would be trained as a missionary or educator. There I would find my Christian husband, who would also be in training for some type of ministry. In the meantime, I would attend church regularly and enjoy a social life of Sunday school, Missionettes, and the much-anticipated entrée to our church youth group, which would occur at the appropriate age of thirteen.

Mom and Dad's rules frustrated me. But despite my variance in opinion, one thing my parents and I agreed on was Jesus. As a child I remember loving the Lord. He was my Savior, my friend. If Mom and Dad's rules were even close to what Jesus commanded, and would ultimately get me to heaven, I would adhere to them. And for a long time I did. Until those teenage years came along—the years Mom would deem as the "alien years." She said it was as if aliens had abducted the daughter she raised and loved and left behind some stranger who made mean faces and said things like *hate* and *no* and *because I don't want to*.

Before the alien years kicked in, I was a sweet, cooperative preteen who enjoyed church and respected my parents, and couldn't wait to become a teenager—mainly for one reason: to join the church youth group.

Joining the youth group was a pivotal event for church kids, as it represented the proverbial next step, an end to adolescence. For years as I advanced through Missionettes in my pink uniform and badge-strewn sash, I envied the teenagers in our youth group. They went on the best social outings: roller skating and skiing, summer Saturdays at the shore. They attended a weeklong overnight youth camp and weekend retreats. And of course, there were boys in the youth group. I counted the years, months, days, and hours.

Finally, when I turned thirteen, I entered youth group.

But during that year, another major event occurred—one that changed the course of my Christian walk for a long time to come. I met Ryan. My first love. And I met him in the last place I imagined meeting my first boyfriend: church.

Our youth group sponsored monthly gym nights, where we opened the gymnasium—a large, state-of-the-art facility with basketball courts, wall-to-wall carpeting, and locker rooms—to the entire neighborhood. My first youth pastor, an enthusiastic young man named Darren, was fresh out of Bible school and had an intense burden to reach the lost. He advertised those nights as First Fridays. He and the older youth would hang flyers all around the neighborhood and partner with other church groups to draw teenagers from every corner of south Philadelphia. Teens from various backgrounds, religions, and family compositions would come, all looking for a hangout, an outlet, something fun, organized and safe.

On one particular First Friday in September, we had an unusually crowded night, with more than one hundred kids pouring in from all four entrances of the gym. The lazy, unsystematic days of summer had run their course and everyone seemed to yearn for something structured.

I stood in the corner by the locker rooms, watching the kids enter. A group of at least ten boys sauntered in through the entrance farthest to my right, directly beneath the basketball net. They were loud and obnoxious, tanned, with dark hair and dark eyes. They came into our gym dribbling basketballs as if they owned the place, wearing oversized shorts and T-shirts, expensive sneakers, and hats turned backward. They all looked the same, walked the same, talked the same. All except one: he had the reddest hair I had ever seen, especially for a boy. I heard his friends call him Reds.

My heart pounded in my chest. Even from clear across the room, I thought everything about him was beautiful: the smile that spread across a mouthful of perfect white teeth, the way his loose clothes were draped on his body, how he walked so nonchalantly, almost oblivious to anything around him.

I had no experience with physical attraction or "liking" boys. I had no idea what I was supposed to feel. But when I saw him, I felt something special and different, a vague but potent curiosity that I wanted to pursue. If there is such a thing, it was definitely love at first sight.

I watched carefully as he assembled himself in a circle with his friends, whacking one of them on the head, stealing a hat from another, bursting into a fit of laughter as another grabbed him by the neck in a headlock. He seemed so playful and fun. I had to know him. Surely I could at least talk to him without crossing any of Mom and Dad's boundaries.

I must have been staring pretty obviously, because when his glance finally shifted my way he looked once and then again, as if to make sure I was really looking. When he was sure, we just stared at each other, intrigued, surprised. Amazed that there may in fact be a mutual interest. After several moments of staring, I smiled—a flirty, welcoming smile that encouraged his pursuit. *Come talk to me*, it said.

His eyes widened. Then he returned my smile with a flirty one of his own that said, *Here I come.*

I watched him make his way over, meandering closer to me, his eyes scanning the crowd but always returning to me, pressing through the noise and laughter, weaving through groups of girls and huddles of guys, even side-stepping the adult leaders—clear across the room to greet me. If my knees weren't locked in panic, I would have met him halfway; but I stood numb in place like a figurine, awaiting the arrival of the redheaded stranger.

I expected something profound to come from his mouth, something ingenious, words that I'd remember forever. "Hi," he said when he finally arrived.

"Hi," I replied, feeling my face redden and watching his do the same.

We exchanged our names, ages, schools, and other thirteen-year-old pleasantries like favorite music, foods and colors. We

I Took the Long Way Home

chatted and smiled and laughed in what seemed to be five of the most significant minutes in my life thus far. The two of us were smitten. An instant connection.

All too soon we were interrupted by the blast of Pastor Darren's bullhorn as he silenced the crowd with a boom so loud that it caused many of us to cup our ears with our hands. He welcomed the new teens to the church, expressed his thankfulness for their attendance, and asked another leader to open the night with prayer.

The leader prayed for the night, for "every person and every family represented, every new brother and sister from other church congregations," and asked the Lord to bless our time. The prayer lasted only a few seconds, and during much of it my eyes were closed reverently, except for one moment when I glanced at Ryan—just to see if his eyes were also closed—and found him looking back at me. He shut his eyes quickly as if I'd caught him cheating on a test. But once the leader said, "Amen," I noticed a sheepish smile on his face.

"I saw you peeking," I teased.

He smiled more broadly, his face turning pink.

While the gym was still reasonably quiet, the pastor listed the rules for the night: no cursing or horseplay; obey all leaders' instructions; play fairly. He then separated the group by gender—girls on one side of the gym and boys on the other. Ryan and I exchanged a look when nearby leaders instructed us to go quickly to our respective sides, silently assuring each other that we'd "talk later."

We played organized games that night, such as Freeze Tag, Dodge Ball, and my personal favorite, Steal the Bacon, with girls winning two out of five games. I occasionally spotted Ryan looking over his shoulder at me—sometimes sticking his tongue out at me when the girls lost. We smiled and made silly faces at each other from across the room. For a thirteen-year-old, it was nothing less than a perfect night.

Then, like a whirlwind, it was all over. Ten o'clock never came so fast. It was like we blinked and our parents were flooding the room to pick up us kids. Leaders marched through the gym like police, escorting neighborhood kids through exit doors, barking orders at us to reduce chaos and safely end the successful social event.

I watched as most of the teens and parents exited, like a wave gathering unbeatable momentum and gradually moving toward the doors. I saw the top of Ryan's bright hair among the departing crowd, moving toward me but against the current, struggling to swim upstream when the current clearly flowed down. Then I lost him, as if he'd been swept away by a rushing tide.

And then I spotted my dad coming toward me, greeting several other parents along the way.

My eyes searched the crowd once more for the speck of red I lost, but Ryan was gone. I felt like Cinderella, with my Prince Charming being carried away by the masses, and my chariot only a few seconds from turning into a pumpkin.

As disappointment flooded my heart, I felt a tap on my shoulder. I turned to find a rough-looking boy with a hat turned sideways, half tucked-in tank top, and a big gold chain dangling from his neck. He looked annoyed, his eyes narrow and mouth tight. "My buddy likes you," he said. His voice was raspy, as if he'd experienced more in thirteen years than some do in a lifetime. "You like 'im or what?" he asked, chewing a mouthful of gum.

I shrugged and then nodded.

"Cool. Here's his number," the boy said matter-of-factly, holding out a scrap of paper. "He wants you to call him."

My heart thumped as I grabbed the paper and shoved it in my pocket. As soon as I did, the boy vanished.

My mind raced. *Call him?* I'd never called a boy. What would I do, what would I say? How could I disobey Mom and Dad? That night I deliberated on whether or not to pursue any type of communication with Ryan. Mom and Dad had clearly prohibited anything even remotely close to dating. "Absolutely no boyfriends," Dad said. "You'll have plenty of time to date in college. Concentrate on your schoolwork and trust the Lord." But Dad didn't know how nice Ryan seemed. And he didn't realize how incredibly responsible I was at thirteen. *Mom and Dad are out of touch with reality*, I decided. I would call Ryan.

The next day I called him from a payphone three blocks from my house. I spent ten quarters on our first phone conversation. We talked about everything, from school to parents to summer vacations. Before we knew it nearly an hour had passed. Our conversation was easy and natural, like I was talking to my brother. I knew I had to talk to him again the next day, or maybe every day. I explained the deal with Mom and Dad, how he'd have to call at scheduled times and immediately hang up if Dad answered. We tried to cover all the bases. If this happens, we'll do this. If that happens, we'll do that. Whatever he had to do was fine with him.

Before we hung up, he asked me a question I didn't quite understand. "Will you go with me?"

"Go where?"

"You know, like go out . . . be my girlfriend."

Girlfriend? It was a word I'd only heard about from older friends and family members. Never did I dream of being someone's girlfriend at thirteen years old. I was never so excited in all my life. I hastily accepted the role, not sure of its implications. All I knew was that I'd picked up the phone to call a guy I met at church and hung up as someone's girlfriend. If Mom and Dad only knew...

It was an innocent relationship, but certainly not within the boundaries of my parents' tolerance. They could not know about Ryan and me. To ensure they didn't find out, I mastered the skill of lying, with my younger brother as my willing accomplice. Whenever Ryan called and I didn't answer, he'd ask for Michael. Michael would then give me a nod or a wink and walk to the basement with the cordless phone. I'd follow him nonchalantly, while my parents watched TV or read or cooked. Once the coast was clear, I'd snatch the phone from him, scoot him out of the room, and commence my conversation.

To make sure I saw him regularly, I convinced Ryan to attend youth group on Wednesdays and Friday-night social events. Ryan didn't come from a Christian home, so the format of our services was somewhat strange to him. However, after a month or so of regular attendance he grew to enjoy it. One Wednesday-night service he prayed with Pastor Darren and even asked Jesus into his heart, though I'm not sure he fully understood why.

Instead of youth group drawing us closer to Jesus, it became an agent for us to see each other. And before I knew it, my commitment to God seemed to come second to Ryan.

It didn't take long for Pastor Darren to notice the connection between Ryan and me, and it didn't take long for Mom and Dad to suspect Ryan was more than just a friend.

Dad started asking who he was, why he called the house, what he wanted, why he walked me to the car after church; he even demanded to know why Ryan attended youth group. I insisted that he was a kid from the neighborhood who'd gotten *saved* (the operative word) and started attending. No threat, no danger—just a nice young man who wanted to know more about Jesus. Because the phone calls seemed harmless and the youth group outings were always heavily supervised, Dad relented.

But eventually talking on the phone and seeing each other at youth group wasn't enough for Ryan and me. We wanted to be alone together. So we took an even greater risk and started scheduling rendezvous, which meant I had to lie about my whereabouts to Mom and Dad.

What began as just a small compromise—a phone call—turned into a network of lies. I would tell Mom I was going to the park with a girlfriend but meet Ryan there instead. On my way to a friend's house, I would meet him at the local candy store, Gloria's Sweet Shop, and share mouthfuls of bubble gum and candy cigarettes.

As time went by, he began writing me love letters and poems, held my hand while we walked, hugged me at the beginning and end of each of our get-togethers. We sometimes shared licks of the same ice cream cone, and for a girl who would only drink from a straw because she refused to put her lips on a glass, this was big. Once, we even dared to give each other a peck on the lips. Without warning, the innocent relationship we started with was transforming into something more.

After a whole school year of going out with Ryan, hugging and holding hands—even saying I love you—I knew we were ready for the next level.

"I think we should kiss," I told Ryan one afternoon when we had each walked fifteen blocks to meet the halfway mark between our houses. "I mean really kiss."

Eyes wide, he asked, "You mean French?"

I nodded.

"When, where?"

"I don't know. Someplace special, somewhere we'll always remember. You pick. Surprise me."

He crinkled his brows, considering the assignment with careful eyes that moved away from my face and back, then nodded. "Tomorrow," he said, grinning broadly and promising me something extra special.

"I can't wait," I told him.

That night I couldn't sleep as I thought about the first real kiss I would soon experience. Part of me bubbled over with

I TOOK THE LONG WAY HOME

excitement and anticipation, while another part of me felt uneasy. I wondered if kissing a boy was something I should wait to do. Looking back, I know that the uneasiness I felt was the Holy Spirit's conviction. Unfortunately, I ignored that conviction and settled for my own understanding.

The next day Ryan asked if I'd meet him at our usual midway point after school. I told Mom and Dad that I was meeting a friend for Italian water ice and Philadelphia-style soft pretzels, and that I'd be home for dinner. They agreed and, without hesitation, I was off to meet the boyfriend no one knew I had.

It was a hot and muggy day in early June and as I walked the fifteen blocks from my house to the halfway mark. I could feel beads of sweat form on my back, where my hair hung atop a sleeveless yellow shirt. I wondered, as I walked, if the sweat came from my nerves or the heat or a combination of both. As I neared our meeting point, my hands were pink and clammy and my heart pounded as I imagined our lips locking. I could hardly believe what was going to happen.

When we finally met, Ryan held a cellophane-wrapped handful of roses—the kind that die after a day. I figured he'd bought them along the way from a street vendor for five dollars or less. But it didn't matter. I had never received roses from anyone before, and to me they were the most beautiful flowers in the world. He handed them to me and kissed my cheek gently. "For you," he said as if we were headed to the prom.

"Thank you." I accepted them graciously.

After standing there basking in our tender moment, he motioned me to follow him. He had an excited look on his face, as if he couldn't wait to show me the Someplace Special he'd found, and anxiously wanted to gain my approval.

We walked to a nearby park, only a three-block distance from our midway meeting point, following a long cement trail that led us through overgrown bushes and eventually dumped us onto a narrow cobblestone walkway that came to a dead end beneath three giant oak trees. It was quiet there, still and charming. The buzz and roar of the city seemed to elude this cozy cut of forest. We stopped at two wooden benches beside those trees; each had a single red rose on it. I smiled. "Did you put this here?"

He nodded.

"How? When?"

"I ran," he joked, grabbing my waist and pulling me close for a hug. I wrapped my arms around his neck and squeezed. I felt his heart thumping against mine. I couldn't wait for what came next.

Before I knew it, he cupped my cheek in his hand, brought my face close to his, and gently planted his fleshy lips onto mine. We stood there like statues—two inexperienced youngsters trying to keep up with adult feelings, exchanging kisses and *I love yous* when neither of us had a clue what either really meant.

Part of me hoped I could somehow make life pause until I was ready to give up the simplicity of being in love for the first time. But as the summer moved at lightning speed and finally came to a close, another side of me burst in anticipation of what lay ahead. Part of me wanted much more than Ryan and church and a confined, predictable life. I couldn't wait to get to high school.

8   High School Drama

High school was like nothing I had ever experienced.

For the first nine years of my student life, from kindergarten to eighth grade, I attended a Christian academy with a student body of no more than 175. The school was run by our church, where my dad served as assistant pastor. Teachers knew me as Pastor Tony's daughter or simply *the pastor's kid*. Because the school and church shared the same building, it felt like I lived there. The church/school was truly my second home.

Both Mom and Dad worked there in some capacity. While most kids were dropped off at school by their parents, or took the bus, my family went there together every day. For many years, Mom served the school as "bus mom," driving the school van, picking up children from all corners of south Philadelphia each morning to get them to school. Dad helped with all kinds of tasks. His position as pastor kept him busy with office work, counseling, visitation, and studying, but his servant's heart kept him willing and available to help the school whenever there was a need. During my time as a student there, he substituted for just about every job in the school: teacher, secretary, janitor, lunchroom monitor, interim school administrator—you name it. There was no escaping him. When he was anywhere in the vicinity, my classmates were sure to tell me. "Psst," someone would hiss. "There goes your dad." *Yeah, thanks, Einstein,* I wanted to reply. As if I hadn't seen him a mile away.

Well, that was grade school. High school was going to be different. No longer was I in a school where my father worked and served on the board. No longer did my dad drive me to and from school every day. No longer was I under the watchful eye of teachers and administrators who never missed an opportunity to threaten to tell my father what I did or didn't do. For the first time, I'd be just another kid, shuffled in like cattle with all the other new students. For once, I wouldn't be *the pastor's daughter*. I could finally fit in; I'd just be me.

It felt good to be nobody—no pressure, no expectations. No one would even know my father's profession. He could be a rock star for all they knew. High school would be my redemption.

I went to an all-girls public high school, the last one in the country and, at the time, one of the most prestigious schools in Philadelphia.

I knew only one other person who would be going there: my best friend, A'nanni, a stick-thin Ethiopian girl with walnut-colored hair, perfect brown skin, and exotic features. We'd known each other since the fourth grade and had graduated from our Christian academy in a class of only ten other students. We became inseparable in middle school, bound by our corny jokes, strict parents, big dreams, and our obsession with earning high honors. I loved her—despite my jealousy that she was the only person in middle school who never experienced an outbreak of pimples. She was my partner in crime, my equal. And with the glimpse of independence shining brightly before us, we were both excited to begin this journey of discovery and adventure in our new school.

Our first brush with freedom came through public transportation. A'nanni and I had to ride the Broad Street subway line to and from high school. I didn't even know what the subway looked like. I knew it thundered beneath us, thrashing gusts of air upward as we walked over the street vents, but I'd never ventured down there.

Dad and Mom were surprisingly agreeable to me riding the subway. A'nanni's mom, a conservative, well-respected woman my parents adored, assured them that we'd be fine. A'nanni's older sister, Sehai, had taken the subway for two years without a problem. Their mother's assurance was all it took to convince them.

A week before the first day of school, Sehai gave us the lowdown on how to ride the subway. Behaving as the epitome of wisdom that A'nanni and I esteemed her as, she gave us a few minutes of her precious time. "Okay, here's the deal," she began. "You need to take the local northbound to the City Hall stop. Get off there and get on the express train northbound to the Olney Avenue stop. Once you get off at Olney, walk one street north and you'll be there."

She repeated the instructions only once. "Got it?"

We got it. And by the time the first day of school rolled around, we were ready.

A'nanni and I met at our usual halfway spot, Blockbuster Video, armed with book bags, subway tokens, and lunch money.

We were filled with nervousness, but bursting with excitement. We couldn't get to the subway tunnel fast enough.

The warm, muggy air seemed to swallow us as we marched down the dirty cement stairs toward the tracks. We descended into a dark, grungy hole in the ground, with orange-and-white ceramic tiled poles lined symmetrically along the seemingly endless island of concrete that separated the north and southbound train tracks.

A'nanni giggled for several minutes and I couldn't stop chatting. If the talking and laughing weren't bad enough, between the two of us, we must have repeated the directions to each other five times. "Local northbound to City Hall, then northbound express train to Olney Avenue.

As we stood there releasing our nervous energy, I counted at least ten other first-timers. They checked the sign a dozen or more times, just to make sure they'd board the right train. They didn't sit. Didn't talk to anyone. They wore book bags and bright white sneakers, and held small scraps of paper—no doubt scribbled with words like *Local to City Hall, northbound express to Olney Avenue*. They were mirror images of us.

Thank God for A'nanni, I thought. At least we had each other.

After what seemed an eternity of waiting, we heard a dull rattling coming toward us from the dark tunnel. Benches slowly emptied all around us, young professionals and students inching close to the tracks.

The noise grew louder and a fierce shrieking squealed forth. I saw two lights in the distant darkness, shaking in our direction like jittery fireflies. As the train rumbled past us and halted to a stop, a gush of wind sent our hair flailing like unruly flames. Patting down my teased strands, I checked the signs in the train car and saw in green letters: *Local North*. A'nanni and I clutched our book bags and followed the other passengers as they swarmed the doors. We newcomers were pushed to the back of the line, the last to enter.

We managed to find two seats together in a relatively cool and surprisingly clean train car. The train was quiet except for a few hushed conversations. Then we started to move.

As we traveled northbound up Broad Street, other trains whizzed past us in both directions. I felt as if we were suspended in air, floating above imaginary tracks. To the other passengers it must have been routine. But to me, it was more than a subway ride; it was the beginning of my independence. I was almost too excited to breathe.

Each time the subway car stopped, a flood of passengers piled in and positioned themselves wherever they could find a spot. The train filled until it was standing room only. At each stop, I checked the signs to make sure I didn't miss our stop. The only one that mattered to me: City Hall. Once we arrived there, we departed the train. To my amazement, the northbound express train was right there, as if it were waiting for me to arrive. We boarded the express, and seven stops later, we made it to the Olney Avenue Station.

We followed the crowd of students pouring out onto the subway platform toward a wide, tiled exit. It looked like a big mall, with mazes and corridors, and people scrambling in different directions.

We approached the bank of escalators. Sehai's instructions were to take the one to the far left. Of course it was the most packed. Like a herd of sheep being transported to the slaughterhouse, we ascended, jostling against one another. When the shiny doors opened to the brilliance of the surface, fresh, bright air engulfed us. We barreled off the escalator.

I couldn't wait to get to my new school.

The building was large and intimidating. It stood atop several acres of sprawling greenery, with a stone wall that enclosed the building and athletic fields. Had it not been for the urban landscape surrounding the school, the roaring cars whizzing through the streets, and the screeching brakes of buses at stop signs, I'd have sworn we were in the heart of the suburbs.

As I marched up those stone steps, book bag slung over my right shoulder and best friend beside me, my heart danced with exhilaration. I couldn't wait to start my new adventure. I strolled into that building like a queen, oozing with confidence, because I knew it all and, more importantly, I had a boyfriend!

But I learned quickly that I was a peon compared to the other girls. My experience with Ryan meant nothing, child's play compared with what some other girls were doing. Girls in ninth grade talked about the fifth and sixth guys with whom they'd had sex. Guys with names like Vinny and Jamal. Older guys who hung out on corners and drove Mustangs. While I had a few kisses under my belt with one boyfriend, these girls were having sex regularly, and they talked about it like it was normal.

I was terrified of the claims they made, the stories they told, the nonchalant attitude about their actions. I came from an ultraconservative home. So conservative that when my mom told me, with bright red cheeks, that men and women had sex for the first time on their wedding night, I agonized over the thought of being naked in front of another person. To quell my anxiety, Mom told me that I could have sex with my clothes on. (I guess it was her way of ending an uncomfortable conversation.) But these girls seemed wild and free. Free from all inhibition and insecurity. They would walk naked in Times Square, I was sure.

My new classmates strode through the hallways with pins on their book bags that read "Girls Rule" and "Go to hell, world, I'm a woman." I even heard they drank beer on the weekends and had fake IDs. They went to dance clubs and listened to the Rolling Stones and Run DMC, smoked Marlboro cigarettes, and rolled joints. They wore makeup and earrings, high-heeled boots and leather trench coats. Their nails were polished with funky colors: blue and red and orange. Their parents let them stay out late, till ten o'clock on school nights and midnight on weekends. No one went to church or youth group. They partied. It made me realize how uncool I was.

This was a whole new world for me, one in which I felt terrified but also intrigued. This world seemed glamorous. The girls. The parties. The boyfriends. The clothes. The confidence they exuded. It all seemed so much better than what I had to offer.

Despite my feelings of inadequacy, A'nanni and I made friends quickly in our school. A group of us called ourselves the United Nations—the UN Girls. Nine of us represented virtually every nationality: Italian, Ethiopian, Indian, African-American, Chinese, Philippine, Korean, Puerto Rican, and Polish Jew. We were the innocent newcomers, the good girls interested in schoolwork, dean's lists, and making our parents proud. We hung out, visited one another's lockers, and sat together at lunch. The wildest thing we did as a group was sneak off to McDonald's between classes for soda and fries, and go to the Gallery Mall in Center City Philly on our way home from school.

Though most of us knew nothing about it, the topic of sex surfaced occasionally in our conversations. Perhaps it was due to our curiosity about the unknown, or our desire to assimilate with the girls who spoke of it as if it were some type of conquest. For us sex was an area of bewilderment. None of us even wanted to imagine herself actually *doing it*. Except Evelyn, whose nickname was Darling.

Darling was the only girl in our group who had actually experienced sex. She'd done it with her nineteen-year-old boyfriend and gladly told us every detail. Where, when, how many times, how it felt, even how it sounded. Many of us cringed or said things like *Ew* when she described such intimate details. Of Puerto Rican descent, Darling was the prettiest of the group, with bronze skin and green eyes. She wore makeup regularly and her hair was always curled, crimped, and highlighted. She wore tight jeans and flashy shirts that flaunted her cleavage. She was even on birth-control pills, which she carried to school and popped in her mouth at lunchtime.

Since Darling and I were the only two with boyfriends, we often exchanged stories. She'd tell me about her man, and I'd talk about my Ryan, how he had kissed my neck and my ear, how his hands had once grazed my bottom. But my stories were boring compared to hers. She described sexual encounters that I never knew existed. "It's the best feeling in the world," she told me. "Nothing compares to it." She made her sin sound beautiful.

I couldn't imagine having sex before marriage. It was like the greatest of all sins, the one that if committed would send me straight to hell for all eternity. The other sins—lying, coveting, gossiping—took a backseat, in my opinion, to this whopper of sins. I'd promised myself and God when I was a little girl that I would save myself for marriage. And even amidst a school of rampant promiscuity, I'd stand by that promise. There was no way I'd compromise.

By the end of the first month of school, A'nanni and I had learned the entire subway route. We knew the bums, the underground musicians, the interchanges—even some above-ground routes.

Our group, the UN Girls, rode the subway to and from school every day together. The forty-minute ride from the edge of south Philly to the heights of north always had something stimulating to jump-start our days. A brawl between kids from rival schools. A lover's spat. Who's dating whom. Who's no longer dating. Fresh gossip almost daily. The subway was like our daytime nightclub. All the cool people rode the subway, including boys from the neighboring co-ed high schools and

I TOOK THE LONG WAY HOME

universities like LaSalle and Temple. Boys were everywhere. Cute boys. Older boys.

One in particular stood out. He was a sixteen-year-old junior at one of the neighboring high schools. Dark and stocky, with intense eyes and spiked black hair, he always rode alone and never sat. Even if every seat was unoccupied, he'd stand in a doorway. He stared at me, with this unwavering look of interest, sometimes positioning himself directly in front of me. I tried ignoring him, but every time I looked his way, I found him staring back at me, sometimes with a devilish grin.

All the girls noticed. "Why does that guy stare at you all the time?" one asked.

"Who cares why?" another said. "He's a cutie!"

He was definitely cute. There was something attractive and puzzling about him. I didn't know anything about him—not even his name. The girls and I called him the Stare Man. Even though I was Ryan's girlfriend, I had to find out who this guy was, what he was about.

One ordinary Monday morning, he made his move. As our train reached its destination, the platform filled with its usual disembarking passengers. Our crew spilled forth and raced to the escalators. My friends all rushed ahead. I was several feet back, fiddling with my gym bag and book bag. As I draped one strap around my shoulder and another around my chest, *he* walked up beside me. The Stare Man wore baggy jeans and black sneakers and a short-sleeved, striped Polo shirt, with a long-sleeved white shirt underneath. He smelled like a grown man, his cologne radiating from his clothes and onto mine. He was the picture of charisma and charm.

"Need help?" he asked as those intense eyes peeked out beneath the shade of a blue Gap hat.

Heat rose to my cheeks. "I'm okay."

"What's your name?" he asked as we pressed our way through the moving crowd.

"Stephanie."

He smiled and stared at me as I rushed to the escalator. He inched closer, grazing his arm against mine. He stepped onto the escalator with me, and before I knew it, he was squashed beside me as we rode up the escalator with dozens of other students.

As we ascended his eyes fixated on me.

"What?" I giggled, my face burning.

"I like you."

My cheeks grew even hotter. Ryan would never be as assertive as this guy.

"You don't even know me."

"I want to." He smiled.

"I don't even know your name."

"Steven."

What did this guy want with me? Maybe it was that "one thing" Dad said all guys wanted. Since Dad never really said what that was and I was too embarrassed to ask, I assumed he meant sex.

Steven made me feel awkward, nervous, not like my Ryan, with whom I could burp and tell jokes. This guy seemed intent, experienced. As we rode the escalator, his eyes never left me. I tried to ignore him, but he just seemed to stare more earnestly.

"What are you staring at?" I finally asked.

"You."

I wanted to say something edgy, something mysterious, but nothing came to mind.

Thankfully, he initiated the questions. He asked my age. My neighborhood. I answered him unreservedly as we walked off the escalator and into the sunny warmth of autumn.

"What's your number?" he asked as we approached the entrance to my school. My heart dropped. What would Ryan think of this older guy asking for my phone number?

"I have a boyfriend," I reported like a good girl.

He winked at me and grinned. "Not for long." Then he wandered ahead of me and joined a group of older-looking boys, who greeted him with handshakes and high-fives.

I watched him, waiting for him to look back—just once—so I could wave him back over to me, just to ask what he meant by *"Not for long."* But he didn't. Not one glance. The crowd seemed to swallow Steven whole. All I could do was hope we would have another encounter.

Ryan and I found it increasingly difficult to see each other. He joined football and could no longer attend Wednesday or Friday night youth services. We saw each other occasionally at Saturday events, but he never had anything interesting to say. Our kisses became less frequent, and his notes bored me. The love I so willingly professed for him dissipated. He was more like a bother than a boyfriend. I wanted more, something like Darling's nineteen-year-old.

I also couldn't stop wondering about Steven. I started planning what I would do when I saw him next. I thought about motioning him over with an alluring tilt of my head and then questioning him confidently. Each morning I chose my outfits carefully and rehearsed the words I might say. All I needed was to see him.

But weeks passed and there was no sign of Steven. I looked for him every day on the subway. I even went from subway car to subway car looking for him. I'd leave home later than usual, and earlier than usual, in hopes of spotting him. But it seemed as if he had vanished.

It wasn't until mid-November, a few days before Thanksgiving break, when Steven resurfaced.

A'nanni and I were sitting in our usual seats, the only private three-seater on the train, which we'd push, shove, and weave our way into each morning. The two of us sat there, giggling about a story we had repeated ten times. Suddenly, A'nanni's eyes widened as she stared over my shoulder. Even before I saw Steven I smelled him. His scent curled into my nostrils before I felt the thump of his bottom hit the seat next to me.

I turned. "Hey," I said with all the confidence I could muster. "Haven't seen you in a while."

"Must not have been looking hard enough," he said.

"Guess not," I said boldly, trying to hide any indication that I had been searching for him.

"Still have that problem?" he asked.

"What problem?"

"The boyfriend."

I nodded.

"Dump him."

"What?"

"Tell him something better came along."

"I'm not telling him that."

"Then give me his number. I'll tell him."

I rolled my eyes but was sure he would do it.

"Can I call you sometime?"

I shook my head. "I'd rather you not."

"Scared you might like me?"

"No." I chuckled.

"Then give me your number."

"I told you I have a boyfriend."

"I guarantee you won't have that problem next week."

"I guarantee that I will."

"If you're so sure then give me your number." He folded his bottom lip under. "Please?"

I stared into those eyes and watched his mouth then curl into a smile. Without meaning to, I blurted out my number. I heard A'nanni gasp.

"I'll call you tonight," he said confidently as he stood to move to the next train car.

I went home that day wondering what time Steven would call. I hovered by the phone all evening. My parents had finally gotten used to Ryan calling, but this guy would be a different story. Surely they would be able to see right through the phone and know that he was an older, more experienced guy—one who'd better stay far away from their innocent little girl.

By nine o'clock, I gave up on the prospect of hearing from Steven. No one called that late on a weekday, unless there was an emergency. I started to head up to my room but before I reached the third step, the phone rang. I nearly stumbled down the stairs. My parents looked up from their reading and exchanged curious glances. I made a nosedive for the phone, calling out, "I'll get it!" I answered breathlessly.

"Yo," said the voice on the other end. It was him.

If this was any indication on how our relationship would be, I should have hung up immediately. If I had any sense, I would've said, "Sorry, I don't speak to men who can't articulate a formal greeting," and hung up. But who knew? Mom and Dad had been so busy teaching me to love God, they forgot to tell me how a man should treat a woman.

"Who is it?" Dad asked.

"It's for me," I answered, cupping the phone into my hand.

"I didn't ask who it was for; I asked who it was."

"A friend from school."

"Don't be long," Dad called before resuming his reading.

"Is this a bad time?" Steven asked.

"Kinda," I said. "What's up?"

"Just wanted to give you my phone number. You can call me whenever you want. I have my own line."

I assured him I'd call when I could and possibly see him in the morning.

"There's one more thing," he uttered before hanging up.

I couldn't imagine what he was going to say.

"I meant what I said when we first met."

· I TOOK THE LONG WAY HOME

In that moment, I tried to replay his words that day on the escalator.

"I like you," he continued. "And I really want to get to know you."

A smile spread across my face. "We'll just have to see about that."

I hung up, exhilarated. I thought of him all night. It took only a thirty-second phone call to convince me that Steven was the guy for me.

Fittingly, I phoned Ryan the next afternoon and told him I didn't want to be his girlfriend anymore. "I'll always love you," I assured him, repeating some scripted line I'd heard from a movie, but not really sure what it meant to *always love someone*. "I just don't want to be tied down during high school." I said it all with such conviction that I almost believed it.

Hanging up with Ryan, I called Steven and assured him that I no longer had *the problem*.

"Good," he told me, "because I don't share."

9

Steven's Girl

Two days after we first talked on the phone, on the day before Thanksgiving, Steven and I were alone for the first time.

Mom had been preparing for days to have her family and Dad's relatives over to our house for Thanksgiving. She had a ton of things to make: lasagna, baked ziti, escarole, spinach balls, ham and, of course, turkey. Michael and I knew better than to even attempt to help. She was a phenomenal cook, and she had everything worked out. "You two find something constructive to do after school tomorrow," she told Michael and me. "You'll just be in the way here."

That was fine with me.

Steven and I rode the subway home together after the half day of school. The train was mobbed with eager teenagers, crammed in like a flock of sheep, baaing with obnoxious laughter and yelling. By the time Steven and I boarded the train, there wasn't a seat anywhere. We stood in an open area by one of the doorways. Within two stops, the doorway filled with standing passengers. The more bodies that squeezed in, the closer Steven and I stood to each other, our bodies jolting forward and backward with every stop and start of the train. His hand grazed mine whenever the train moved.

"You okay?" Amid the deafening noise of the train and the irritating cackle of those around us, his voice was consoling and engaging.

"Yeah."

He slipped his warm hand into mine and held it tightly, as if I already belonged to him. At that moment I was sure I did.

Our hands and fingers remained interlocked for the rest of the ride and even as we disembarked and made our way above ground.

With no official destination, we crossed the street and cut through a half-empty school parking lot. The neighborhood high school was a massive, pallid-stoned building with a huge mural covering the wall facing the lot. The image was of a black ballerina surrounded by brilliant pastel colors. Her powerful, shapely legs stretched across the brick canvas in a classic dancer stance. I imagined the students had painted it as a permanent solution to the long-standing graffiti problem. Though the school was both mine and Steven's neighborhood high school, neither Steven's parents nor mine would dream of sending us there. It wasn't prestigious enough.

We walked through the lot slowly, snaking through cars, dodging mounds of leaves and trash that collected in uneven segments of gravel and pavement. The cold air crept through my coat and hair, nagging at my skin. My body shivered, teeth chattered, and arms shook.

Noticing my discomfort, Steven stopped me in mid-step, wrapped his arms around me, and moved them up and down my back to warm me. "Feel better?" he asked, his mouth close to my ear. I nodded. Grabbing me by the shoulders and positioning his face in front of mine, he said, "I want you to be my girl."

I didn't say a word. I just gazed at his dark, puzzling eyes as his lips curled up in a smile. Suddenly the air didn't feel so cold. He leaned his forehead against mine and hugged me. Everything around us seemed to recede in the warmth of his arms. His face moved close to mine, and he kissed me. His tender lips pressed onto mine for several moments.

"Be my girl," he said again as his lips moved away from mine. I nodded, titled my head, and smiled. "Okay."

It was official. I was Steven's girl.

I could hardly believe I was dating a junior in high school! Me—the virgin freshman, the pastor's daughter. It made my relationship with Ryan seem miniscule, insignificant. I had graduated from the minor leagues. Steven was the real deal, the Majors.

From that point on, the two of us were inseparable. Every chance I got, any moment I could steal away from my family, I'd see him. If Mom sent me to the corner store for vegetables, Steven met me there. If I walked to an aunt's house to deliver a can of tomatoes, I stopped at Steven's for a kiss.

He told me he loved me within two weeks of dating. "I've never felt this way about anyone," he said. "I want you to be with me forever." His words sounded sincere. There wasn't a shred of doubt that what we had was true love.

I thought of him constantly. All day at school, all night at home. Even at lunch with the girls. I missed him terribly whenever we were apart. With Ryan, I'd been in control. I could walk away from the relationship at any moment and not feel the least bit grieved. But Steven was my world.

The more serious Steven and I became as a couple, the more I looked to Darling for advice. I told her about my conviction not to have sex outside of marriage. I also told her that Steven didn't share that conviction.

"You can't keep him waiting forever," she said. "He'll move on to some pretty little thing who's gonna give him some."

I couldn't bear the thought of losing him. "But I really want to wait until marriage."

"If you truly love him, why wait? Sex brings you much closer as a couple. When me and my Andrew started having sex, it brought us to a new level. It's like we're already married."

"But you're not."

"But someday maybe we will be. And even if we never get married at least we shared something special together."

It sounded nice. But I wondered, what if Andrew decided to leave Darling, or vice versa? Would she have sex with her next boyfriend? And the next? What if she got pregnant or caught some disease? It seemed too much of a risk.

"I want to wait for my husband."

"You can wait if you want," she said with attitude, placing both hands on her hips. "But don't expect him to wait for you. He has needs. And if you're not gonna meet them, he'll find someone who can." *Fine,* I thought. I'd rather lose out on some allegedly delightful experience than lose my virginity.

Still, I tucked Darling's words in my heart.

Though I stood firm on my resolve not to have sex, I started to compromise in other areas. Because Steven had little regard for anything related to church, claiming that he talked to God on his own terms, I no longer wanted to attend youth group, and I had little patience for family devotions.

"I have a big test to study for," I told Dad when he called Michael and me from our rooms for devotions.

"Then we'll pray that the Lord will help you study," he said.

"I don't feel good," I told Mom when it was time for youth group.

"You'll feel better once you get to church," she said.

After service one Wednesday evening, Pastor Darren asked if something was wrong.

"Why do you ask?"

"You seemed distracted during worship. And I believe I heard you sigh when you were called upon to pray."

I assured him everything was fine, trying not to roll my eyes.

"Do you need me to pray with you about anything?"

"No, thanks." I didn't need anyone's prayers. All I needed was Steven.

Mom and Dad questioned my behavior as well. "Is something bothering you, Steph?" Dad asked one night as I lay on my bed waiting for him and Mom to fall asleep so I could call Steven.

"Everything's fine," I replied with an annoyed tone.

He sat on my bed and folded his hands on his knees. "Have you been spending time with the Lord lately?"

My insides coiled in frustration. The only person I wanted to spend time with was Steven.

"I haven't seen you spending any time in the Bible. You used to love God's Word."

"I'm just really busy, Dad," I said. "It's not easy getting the grades you and Mom want me to get."

"You have to prioritize. The Lord needs to come first in your life. All the other things will follow."

"Yeah, yeah, I know." I stood, hoping he would leave.

"I'd like to pray with you." Dad stood and placed his hand on my shoulder.

I balled my fists. *I don't want prayer!* But I listened quietly to Dad's deep, melodic voice.

His words were nothing I hadn't heard before, but as I listened to him ask the Lord to lead, guide, and strengthen me in my walk, I realized that if I was going to live peacefully in my parents' house, I needed to play the game. Attending church salved my conscience while I lived according to my own reckless standards the rest of the time. What I didn't realize then is that no one can serve two masters.[xxxvi] I couldn't love both God and sin.

Not long into the relationship, Steven became demanding and controlling. He wanted to see me all the time. Talk to me in the middle of the night. Meet for breakfast and hang out after school. I loved the attention. But that meant twice as many lies, twice the sneaking around as I'd done with Ryan.

At the beginning of the school year, I'd joined several clubs at school. My favorite, Public Speaking, met at 7:30 every morning. But when Steven suggested I come to his house before school, I immediately decided to blow off this enjoyable activity.

Steven's parents were divorced and he lived with his father, who worked ridiculous hours: four AM to six PM. So I woke up at six AM on school days to meet Steven at his house.

He had breakfast out for me each morning when I arrived: cereal or a sausage-and-egg omelet, with chocolate milk. While we ate, I imagined we were husband and wife. "Pass the orange juice, honey," I would say.

"Sure, Babe."

It felt so right.

After breakfast, we watched music videos, many of which I'd never seen. As I watched the images on screen, mesmerized by the groping and sensuality depicted, Steven kissed me, his hands wandering over my body, trying to touch all kinds of uncharted territory.

"Stop," I told him, prying his hands off me. "I don't want to."

He whispered all kinds of I *love yous* and I *want yous*, and I told him why I wouldn't and couldn't go any further than kissing and hugging. Sometimes he begged; sometimes he whined. Other times he chugged along as if my words meant nothing. Darling's warnings about meeting Steven's needs rang in my head.

Time was always my saving grace. We would eventually have to leave, and the threat of missing class always seemed to spark his compliance.

We scurried to the subway train, where we nestled in a private two-seater. Sometimes I fell asleep on his shoulder; other times he helped me study for my first-period tests.

I never needed to quiz Steven on any of his exams. He was a straight-A student. Member of the National Honor Society, with a GPA of 3.8, he didn't have to study for hours or pull all-nighters like I did. School came easy to him.

At sixteen, he knew just what he wanted to do with his life. Major in criminal justice at Penn State University, where he hoped to garner a generous academic scholarship. Graduate with honors. Move on to Temple Law School. Work for some big law firm in Center City Philadelphia. Retire at fifty and then travel the world. His determination and passion for life drew me to him. Steven had big plans and I had no doubt he would fulfill each of them. I was proud to be with him.

I TOOK THE LONG WAY HOME

I credited Steven's parents for his tenacity. They both demanded excellence from him. "Education is the way up and the way out," Steven told me. I was certain that the "out" he referred to was his father's house.

His dad, an Italian immigrant, made very little money, but he strove to realize the American dream through his son. For years, Steven's mother was the breadwinner of the family. She started out as a secretary for a doctor when Steven was five years old. Within two years, she ran the entire office. She was uneducated and belligerent, but smart as a whip. Three more doctors joined the small office, and Mrs. Lolio made herself indispensable.

Within five years of taking the job, she left Steven and his father for a six-bedroom home in an elite Philadelphia suburb. Before Steven even knew his parents' divorce was final, his mother sent him a birthday card with the return address reading, "Dr. and Mrs. Roger Donato" and "Love, Mom and Roger" scribbled inside. He hated both of his parents for what happened—his mother for leaving and his father for letting her go. His animosity made him work even harder to succeed in life.

At the end of every school day, I waited outside the front entrance of my school for Steven. I'd see him with a group of other guys his age mounting the hill toward me. Steven always walked toward the back, in his own world, but close enough to be included in theirs. He walked with confidence, even a hint of arrogance. And he was mine.

As they neared my school entrance, their voices grew more robust, with twinges of obnoxious laughter. When they were just inches from me, Steven reached out his hand to grab mine and we'd snap together like Legos. I couldn't imagine life without him.

My big dilemma was Mom and Dad.

They didn't know he was my steady boyfriend, but they were convinced he was trouble. The mere mention of his name brought forth questions and arguments.

"Who is this guy?" Dad questioned.

"A junior in high school," I replied, determined to keep my answers vague. "He lives in the neighborhood."

"Where did you meet him?"

"On the subway."

"Why is he calling you?"

"He's a friend," I said with a shrug.

"I know he's more than just your friend," Mom accused.

Although I did my best to downplay our relationship, they eventually forbade any contact with him. "I don't want him calling here anymore," Dad demanded. "You're too young for a boyfriend."

"God doesn't want us unequally yoked with unbelievers," Mom reminded me.[xxxvii]

"This guy only wants one thing from you, you know."

Blah, blah, blah.

I wished I could introduce him to Mom and Dad so they could see how smart and ambitious he was. Maybe then they would understand why I had to be with him, why I risked so much for him. Then again, I doubted they'd see anything except that their innocent little girl was *dating*. Horror of horrors!

I couldn't imagine why I wasn't allowed to have a boyfriend. I was mature enough. After all, I'd been with Ryan for almost a year. And my relationship with Steven was light years better.

So I decided, for the sake of everyone involved, to lie. I would keep my life with Steven a secret. I figured he was worth it.

10 Idle Threat Theory

As my relationship with Steven grew and my relationship with the Lord and my parents crumbled, a chain of events occurred that precipitated my worst nightmare.

In May of my freshman year of high school, six months into my relationship with Steven, Mom mentioned that Dad would be guest speaking at a church in New Jersey that Sunday, so he wouldn't be attending service with the three of us in Philly. I didn't think much of it. He was a pastor and pastors occasionally spoke at other churches.

A few weeks later Mom told us that Dad was going back to that church and that this time she would accompany him. This waved a major red flag. Mom never missed teaching her Sunday school class. Something was definitely up.

"Why are you both going?" I questioned.

The joyous look on Dad's face floored me. It was as if he were using all his strength just to contain the excitement welling inside him. "The Lord has opened a door for me to be a candidate for a senior pastor position in New Jersey."

"What?" I asked in disgust.

Dad laughed quietly. "There's a church out in Jersey—beautiful facility, great people—with a senior pastor vacancy. Twelve men applied. They chose five final candidates and have narrowed the five down to three."

"And you're one of the three." I crossed my arms.

Dad looked at Mom and nodded. "Yes."

"So what if you're picked?"

"We'll pray about it. See what the Lord wants us to do."

"Do you mean we might move?"

"If the Lord wants us to, yes."

I felt as if a knife had been thrust into my heart. The thought of moving and not seeing Steven anymore made me physically ill. All I could do was hope that they'd pick someone else.

As a formality, Michael and I visited the church with Dad and Mom the following Sunday. The sanctuary was a small building, about half the size of ours. The smell of wood and new carpet slithered into my nostrils as I casually surveyed the room. Rectangular shaped, with long wooden pews and red seat cushions, the chapel was adorned with stained-glass windows and ornate lights hanging from the ceiling. I hated everything about it and wanted nothing to do any church outside of Philadelphia.

A few weeks after Michael and I visited the church, my worst nightmare became a reality. Dad gathered us in the living room for an important announcement. "We're moving."

My brother and I sat there, our mouths open.

"Excuse me?" I said, sure he hadn't said what I thought he did.

"I got *the call*. The New Jersey church board voted unanimously, and a large majority of the congregation agreed. I've accepted the position as senior pastor."

Mom beamed at Dad. "Out of twelve men, including the former pastor's son-in-law, Pastor Tony Cavelli was their top choice."

My parents thanked the Lord, their faces aglow. "The door has been opened," Dad said. "All we need to do is walk on through!"

I couldn't believe it. Just when I'd found freedom, a routine, a boyfriend, a group of friends. I couldn't leave.

Perhaps this was just a threat—Mom and Dad's twisted way of trying to garner my regular and uncomplaining church attendance. If so, I'd promise to attend morning and evening Sunday services, midweek meetings, and youth group outings without protest. I'd even put on a happy face and sit up front with my arms uncrossed and eyes unrolling. I would do anything—as long as we didn't have to move.

"We've already put the house up for sale," Dad said. "And Mom and I found a house in New Jersey that we really like."

So much for the idle threat theory.

"We'll be moving next month," Mom added.

"I can't leave my school," I groaned. "I just started."

"You'll go to a new school," they said in unison.

"What about my friends?"

"You'll make new friends," they added.

"I don't want to make new friends!"

"You'll have to," Dad said, "because we're moving." His tone suggested that they'd had enough of me and my attitude. "It's only about a thirty-five minute drive from here."

Thirty-five minutes by car felt as far away as Alaska.

"I don't want to go," I grumbled.

"You're going," Dad said firmly.

"But you don't need me to preach. Why do I have to go?"

"Because we're a family and the Lord is moving us on as a family."

Terrific. The Lord Himself was taking me away from my life, away from Steven and my friends. I would have to leave all that I knew and start over. In the midst of adolescence, just when I'd begun to find my place in the world, I would be plucked out of my surroundings and thrust into some new, unfamiliar place. I would be all alone. There'd be no A'nanni, no UN Girls. I'd be a stranger, a nomad in search of people who would accept me.

How could my parents —no, how could *God* do this to me?

That same week my father announced our departure to the Philadelphia church family. A formal commissioning service was arranged. The senior pastor of our church prayed over our whole family and commissioned Dad and Mom and Michael and me to full-time ministry. "The Lord has marvelous plans for the Cavelli family," the pastor announced to the congregation. "He will use them mightily."

I was certain his forecast did not include me.

The commissioning service was followed by a farewell dinner given by the church board. More than three hundred church members attended. Dad's friends arranged for all his favorites: favorite song leader to sing his favorite praise chorus, favorite pianist to play his favorite hymn, a reading of one of his favorite passages of Scripture. This was followed by a slide show of pictures that depicted Mom and Dad's faithful service to the Lord. Pictures of Dad surrounded by a wild bunch of teenagers during his days of service as youth pastor. Photos of Mom with her Sunday school students. Dad and Mom serving food at church events. The pictures seemed endless: a photographic display of almost a decade of consistent service to their Savior.

Several elder youth group members commissioned Michael and me to lives that were pure and pleasing to the Lord. Each of the members took a turn reading a Scripture about obeying our parents, maintaining holy lives, seeking first God's kingdom. As I listened, a sting of regret pierced my heart. If I wasn't so attached to Steven, I could sever my ties with him and live a life that was pure and holy, a life void of lies and deceit. But it seemed impossible to part with him. I was in too deep.

The remainder of the dinner was laced with a muddle of sentiments that left me confused, angry, torn. I didn't want to leave. Everything that meant anything to me was in Philadelphia.

I had to break the news to Steven.

"Tell your parents I don't want you to go," he suggested.

"They don't even know I still talk to you." I was sure they had their suspicions, but they had no idea the extent to which I'd been seeing him. Perhaps they figured moving me away to New Jersey would end the relationship for good.

"Well, tell them I'm your boyfriend and that you're coming to live with me."

I rolled my eyes. "You know if it was up to me, I'd never leave."

"It's okay," he said, his voice trailing off. "I'm used to people leaving me."

His words unnerved me. With a fervent gaze, I promised to see him whenever I could. "I'll be back every weekend. I promise."

"You better," he said. "Don't make me come to Jersey and kidnap you."

"Promise you won't date anyone else?"

"*You* better promise," he said. "You're the one leaving. You'll probably meet some football player at your new school."

"Or maybe a baseball player," I joked.

"So you already have me replaced with some guy in tight pants." We laughed for a brief moment, then his expression turned serious. "You're the only girl for me." He kissed my hand gently. "I could never let you be with anyone else."

"And I would never want to," I said, holding back tears.

"Please don't leave."

"If there was any way I could stay, you know I would."

"Then promise you'll never stop loving me."

"Never," I said. "And promise you'll always love me."

"Always," he said.

I had no idea how easily teenage promises are broken and forgotten.

We moved on a Saturday in July. It was a warm day, with a cool, gentle wind wafting occasionally through the air. Mom and Dad were thrilled for the cooperative weather, considering it yet another sign that this was the right thing for us. I'd have preferred a torrential downpour.

Dad's younger brother, Uncle Robert, helped us move. He and his wife, Aunt Jo Ann, were the only other born-again Christians in the family. Dad and Mom led them to the Lord when they first married.

Uncle Robert acted like a drill sergeant. He had us lifting, piling, pulling, dragging—even barricading the street—all before seven AM. "Let's go," he commanded. "Get those boxes, move that chair, stack those crates."

I dragged my feet around the chairs and appliances and stacks of boxes like a zombie, shoulders hunched over, eyes drooping with sadness. In spite of my lack of cooperation, Dad and Uncle Robert had the entire three-story house packed in a U-Haul in less than two hours. I didn't even have a chance to say good-bye to A'nanni.

Mom and I drove in our family car, while Dad, Michael, and Uncle Robert led the way in the U-Haul. I cried the whole ride.

"It's not the end of the world, Steph," my mother said.

But it was the end of my world.

"You'll make new friends."

"I don't want new friends. I want my old friends."

"I know. Believe me, I know." Mom's words poured from her mouth like lava. "I'm leaving my whole family."

"You don't want to move?" I asked.

She shrugged. "I'm happy wherever I am, but…"

"But what?"

"I was just fine where we were."

I sat up straight. "Why didn't you tell Daddy you didn't want to go?"

"Because it wasn't up to him, just like it wasn't up to me. This is the Lord's will for us."

My blood pounded in my veins. "How could it be His will if we don't even want to go?"

"Jesus didn't want to go to the cross, but He did, out of love for all of us. We're following the Lord's will because He knows best; we trust Him."

Part of me had to respect that level of faith. But I still didn't understand why *I* had to move.

We arrived in New Jersey at the onset of summer, just as the tepid temperatures began to rise. We migrated from a small row home in the City of Brotherly Love to a four-bedroom single house, with grass and landscaping, situated amid tall trees and lush bushes.

Our New Jersey town was nothing like the city. It was quiet and still, with chirps of crickets and choruses of cicadas in place of the shriek of buses, the vroom of engines, and the blasting of car horns. I longed for the intimacy and excitement of city life. Here I had no subways or buses to transport me to the mall, no trendy hotspots, no next-door neighbors, no number streets or taxis—just highways and K-Marts and cul-de-sacs. *Yawn.*

That first weekend I begged my parents to take me to the city so I could see A'nanni. Even just for a day, an hour. I'd take whatever I could get. I wanted to go home. I wanted to see Steven. I longed for my former life. But nothing I did or said got me there.

The next weekend was the same. I begged and cried and whined, but nothing.

Finally, the following weekend, they agreed to take me back to Philadelphia for a visit. Mom would drop me off at my aunt's house on Friday morning on her way to work. I could stay in Philly until Monday as long as I went to church on Sunday.

"No problem," I told them.

Within an hour of my arrival, I was headed for Steven's house on foot—it was only five blocks away from my aunt's. He'd just gotten his first car, a red 1990 Toyota Tercel, and he couldn't wait for me to see it. He'd named the car Joyce and talked about her like she was a living, breathing being.

I couldn't wait to see Steven. To smell him, hug him, kiss him. It had been almost three weeks since I'd felt his dry, calloused hands holding mine.

My heart jumped through my skin when I saw him. He was hanging out his front door, with that confident grin of his, wearing a wrinkled T-shirt and baggy shorts that sat just beneath his waist. He greeted me with a hug and kissed me like he hadn't seen me in a year. He smelled like powder and aftershave, a fresh scent that was all his own. "You're not leaving me again," he said, holding me tight. "I'm not letting you go."

"You'll have to," I said. "My dad's picking me up on Monday."

He smiled. "Come on. I want you to meet my Joyce." He slipped his bare feet into sneakers and led me to the corner of his street, where Joyce was parked. She was polished and shined, wheel rims glistening like diamonds. "Get in," he said with pride.

The car smelled like lavender and it was as clean as new. Not a piece of trash, speck of ash, or fleck of dust anywhere. He patted the dashboard as he got in. "This is my girl," he said with a grin. "When you're not around, it's all about her."

I laughed. At least he had something to occupy his time.

We whipped all over south Philadelphia. I wished we could have driven into the proverbial sunset and never come back. I just wanted Steven.

And he wanted me—all of me.

The whole weekend was a constant tug-of-war. I had to peel his hands off me every couple of minutes. "Stop," I told him over and over. "I can't. I don't want to."

"Please, please, I'll do anything," he begged.

After countless attempts at coercion, followed by my repeated assurances that I would not have sex before marriage, he finally seemed to accept my decision.

"We don't have to do it if you don't want to," he said.

"Well, I don't," I assured him. "And I'd appreciate it if you'd stop hassling me about it."

He snickered, promising he wouldn't *hassle* me anymore. Despite his promise, I was certain there would be plenty more battles.

That first weekend came and went fast. Before I knew it, I was back at home in New Jersey, planning and scheming for my next visit to the city.

The following weekend Dad had plans for Michael and me—family plans that required our cooperation and participation. So visiting Philly was out of the question. Steven was not happy.

The next weekend wasn't very promising either.

I made it to the city only two more weekends that summer, and before we knew it Steven was back at school for his senior year and I was off to my new school for my sophomore year.

Though Dad and Mom insisted I would make new friends, it wasn't easy. The students had all grown up together. The cliques of girls were formed long before I got there, and there wasn't much room for outsiders. I made a few friends, but no one comparable to A'nanni or the UN Girls. All I wanted to do was go home.

But going home became more difficult as time passed. As my parents grew more involved with their new church, they got tired of driving me to Philly and back on weekends.

I feared Steven would find someone new to replace me. Though he pledged his love to me in letters and phone calls, I couldn't shake the feeling that he could easily charm another girl the same way he'd charmed me.

Instead he found a different kind of distraction. Cigarettes and alcohol. He told me booze helped him think and cigarettes helped him sleep. The studious, industrious young man I'd fallen for became irresponsible and careless.

Still, my heart clung to Steven. I longed to see him, but could rarely get a ride to the city.

"My parents need me to go to church."

"They won't let me leave."

"I'm grounded."

It was always something.

Finally one weekend Steven told me he'd come get me.

"You know my parents won't let me leave with you," I moaned, clutching the phone receiver.

"Then sneak out."

"I'll get caught."

"Then sneak me in."

That was a thought. My room was the only bedroom on the first floor. It was spacious, with a separate adjoining area for storage, so I really had two rooms, almost like my own apartment. I could blast my music, and they rarely complained. The room also had a window that was fairly close to the ground. "Maybe you can climb in my window," I said without thinking.

"Good. I'm coming right now," he said, then hung up.

I panicked. What was I thinking? The idea of sneaking Steven in made my stomach contract hard.

Dear Lord, help me, I prayed.

Mom seemed equipped with a sixth sense about what I was or wasn't doing. I sometimes wondered if God appeared to her in her dreams and showed her what was about to transpire. One thing was for sure: somehow she'd know there was a strange boy in her daughter's room.

I called back at least twenty times to discourage him but got no answer. I knew there was no stopping him. If I didn't let him in the window, he'd come knocking on the front door.

I TOOK THE LONG WAY HOME

I scrambled upstairs and peeked into my parents' bedroom. Both were sitting in bed, Mom watching the news and Dad reading his Bible. "Good night," I called.

"Night," Dad called back. "Love you."

I checked on Michael. He was in bed, with his headphones on. I waved good night before heading back downstairs to my room. The first floor was quiet. All the lights were out except for Mom's stained-glass nightlight, which illuminated my footsteps as I tiptoed down the hall. My heart raced as I convinced myself that no one would be back down until morning.

I lined the inside of my bedroom door with towels and blankets to muffle the sound of any unfamiliar voices floating through the house.

Then I stood by the window and waited.

For the next thirty minutes I watched every car drive past. It felt like an eternity. Finally I saw Steven's Tercel putt-putting toward my house. He craned his neck out the window, checking the addresses on the curb. He stopped the car in the middle of the street, then pulled over to park.

Nervous sweat drenched my forehead. There was no turning back now.

Relax, I told myself. *Deep breaths.*

Steven emerged from a cluster of overgrown bushes. He strolled along, half a cigarette in hand, looking not the least bit hurried. He saw me through the window and called out, "Hey!"

He might as well have used a bullhorn and announced to the neighborhood that he was sneaking into my house.

As I scolded him in my loudest whisper, he climbed through the window like a monkey and tumbled into the room. He reeked of beer and cigarette smoke.

"Are you drunk?"

"No," he said, laughing. "Well, maybe a little. I had a few beers on the way here."

"You drank while driving?" I whisper-screeched.

"Yeah. I always do. It's no big deal."

"Are you crazy? You could get arrested. You could die."

"I'm not stupid. I know what I'm doing. I'm more alert when I'm drinking. More careful." He kicked off his shoes and tossed his jacket on the floor before flopping onto the bed. No hug or kiss or "I missed you"—just a sigh and "I'm tired."

I glared at him as he coiled under my blankets and shut his eyes. I didn't want to touch him or even look at him. He was an intruder in my parents' home. I wanted him out.

I circled the room a dozen times, listening for footsteps, unfamiliar movements—any smidgen of evidence that my parents were hot on my trail.

My hands shaking, eyes twitching, and heart racing, I finally grabbed a blanket and pillow and settled on the floor.

"Come here," he said drowsily.

"No." I punched the lumpy pillow. "I'm going to sleep."

"Sleep on the bed," he pleaded, "with me."

"No." I was sure if I went anywhere near him a special police task force would burst through my bedroom door with flashlights and handcuffs. I scooted as far away from the bed as possible.

That night was torture. I couldn't sleep a wink. I felt as if I were suffocating alive. I prayed for the Lord to let me get away with this one thing without my parents' knowing. *I'll never do anything wrong again, ever,* I promised. *Just don't let them find out.*

Sometime during the night, I must have dozed off, because the next thing I heard was the front door slamming shut. Daylight skulked through the mini-blinds.

I bounded from my corner of the floor like a jack–in-the-box and crept to the window. Peeking through the blinds I saw my parents climbing into their car. They'd told me they would be leaving early for a minister's conference in north Jersey. I breathed a sigh of relief as the car slid out of the driveway, then watched with elation as they drove out of sight.

I had to get Steven out of the house. I poked and pushed him several times before I finally got him to roll out of my bed. Before he was fully awake, and not without a struggle, I shoved him back out the window into which he'd crawled the night before. Promising God I'd never sneak Steven in again, I thanked Him for bailing me out one more time.

As I watched the Tercel drive off, I decided it was time to end things with him for good.

"I can't be with you anymore," I told him when he called later that day.

"You're not breaking up with me," he said with a sneer.

I argued vehemently that I could never let him in my house again. But he kept telling me why I should, why I wanted to, how we were meant for each other. Against my better judgment, I listened.

The next few weekends I begged my parents to let me go back to the city, mainly to avoid Steven making good on his threat to return to my parents' house. My pleading worked. For a while.

But eventually a weekend came when I couldn't get away. My parents insisted I stay home.

"I want to have family night," Dad said. He and Mom had made plans for dinner, then a trip to the Christian bookstore for Michael and me to pick out a book or cassette, and then we were going to play Scrabble or Monopoly. *Family fun.*

Steven had other plans for my night. He pressured me into letting him come over after midnight.

The second time was less agonizing than the first. The next time was not a big deal at all. What started out as an incriminating crime, which I swore never to repeat, became an easy sin. All it took was a little compromise.

One Saturday morning when Steven had spent the night, about nine, Mom pounded on my bedroom door. Usually, Steven was gone well before nine. But he'd insisted, just this once, on sleeping late.

"Stephanie, open up!" Mom's voice was like a police siren behind a speeding vehicle.

My heart leapt out of my body. I covered Steven with blankets, concealing his head and feet, quietly shut the door to the back storage room where he lay, and ran into the front bedroom. After a quick once-over of the room, I unlocked the door and swung it open.

My mother stood there, glaring at me—her hair a mess, still wearing her night clothes and slippers, the remains of black eyeliner wedged in the corner of her eye.

"Yeah?" I asked.

She pushed me aside and charged into my room. "What's that smell?"

"What smell?"

She circled the room. "Smells like cigarettes." Her nose wrinkled up like a dog sniffing for food. She snapped her gaze at me. "Have you been smoking?"

"No!" I screeched, remembering horridly how Steven had stretched his head out the back window and lit up just a few hours earlier.

She grabbed a corner of my T-shirt and brought it to her face. "You've been smoking!"

"No, I haven't."

"Don't you lie to me! I can smell it."

"I've never smoked a cigarette in my life!"

She looked at me with a crooked frown. "I wasn't born yesterday. I know what cigarettes smell like, and you smell like you've smoked a pack of them."

I decided I'd better go along with it. If I confessed to smoking and got her out of there, she wouldn't find the sleeping beast in the next room. I hung my head in shame.

"Your body's a temple, Stephanie, the temple of the living God.xxxviii You don't need those cancer sticks to feel good."

"I know," I said with whatever remorse I could muster.

"Do we need to have a talk about this?"

"No," I said. "I just wanted to try it once. I promise it won't happen again."

"You have too much going for you to be messing around with those things."

"I'm sorry," I said. She didn't have to convince me. I hated cigarettes.

She nodded her forgiveness. "Look at this room," she said. "It's a mess!" She strode toward the back room and pushed open the door.

My heart pounding, I stared at the mountain of blankets under which Steven was sleeping.

"Half the linen closet's on this floor," Mom barked. She pulled the door shut again and shook her head. "I want this room cleaned today."

She hadn't seen him! Then again, how could she see what she would never imagine being there?

She stepped over piles of clothes and kicked cassette tapes out of her way. She stopped at the front bedroom door and looked back at me one more time. "I don't ever want to smell those things on you again. I don't want cigarettes even brought into this house."

"Never," I said as our eyes locked.

If she only knew what was really in her house.

I TOOK THE LONG WAY HOME

11

Only Fools Refuse to Be Taught^{xxxix}

"Mom," I said one day, standing beside her as she made her signature pasta sauce, "what would you say if I asked to go on birth control pills?"

She whipped her head toward me. "Why are you asking me that?"

"I was just wondering," I said, casually sliding my hand across the countertop. "A lot of my friends' moms made them get on it."

"I'd say absolutely not!" She drove a knife into an onion, slicing it into small chunks. "It's a sin to even think about having sex before marriage. I don't know what kinds of mothers your friends have, but no daughter of mine is going on birth control pills at fifteen."

"I'm almost sixteen."

"I wouldn't care if you were forty. If you're not married, you shouldn't be having sex."

"So you wouldn't care if I were a forty-year-old virgin?"

"I wouldn't care if you were the last virgin on earth, or if you died a virgin. Sex is for marriage, an expression of love between two married people."

"But what if I really loved someone?"

"Doesn't matter. The Bible says it's for marriage. Only."

Mom's bloodshot eyes had dark circles beneath them, and her hair was a mess. She'd been up since five, I knew. The house was spotless, except for the kitchen. The clothes had all been washed, dried, and folded, and the plants watered—all while my brother and I slept.

The Thanksgiving season was upon us, marking my first anniversary with Steven, and once again, Mom was at her post, employing her gift of hospitality.

"All the girls at school are on the pill."

She scraped the chopped onions off the cutting board into a big pot on the stove. "Is that supposed to make me think it's okay? You'd better rethink whatever it is you're thinking," she threatened, bobbing her head from side to side.

"I wasn't thinking anything," I grunted. "I was just wondering."

"Well, now you know." Mom grabbed a jar of garlic salt from the lazy Susan in the cupboard. "This is about that boy from the city, isn't it?"

"No."

"You promised your father you wouldn't speak to him anymore." She slammed the jar down on the counter.

"I don't."

"What do I look like, a moron?" Mom started cutting the tomatoes. "I know what you're doing."

How much does she really know? I wondered.

"Wake up, honey. That boy doesn't love you. He's out to get one thing and he won't give up until he does." She waved the knife at me, dripping tomato juice onto the counter. "Did he put you up to this pill idea?"

"No!"

"But you do still talk to him, don't you?"

"I don't, Mom. I swear to God."

"Only liars have to swear. Is that what you are now?"

"No!"

"I don't even know who you are anymore, Stephanie." She dumped the chopped tomatoes in with the onions.

I stared at the onion peels and tomato tops strewn across the countertop. "You don't understand."

"You're right. I don't." She shook garlic salt over the vegetables in the pot. "Did you really expect me to tell you, 'Sure, go ahead and have sex; as long as you're protected, it's fine with me'? If that's what you thought you'd better think again. As for me and my house, we will serve the Lord."[xl]

I stood there for several moments, unsure of what to say, watching my mom briskly stir the sauce. The air was thick with the rich smell of garlic and tomatoes.

I played with the three empty glass jars Mom had placed on the counter to be filled. Each one was for a shut-in from our church, elderly people who could no longer do much of anything for themselves. Mom visited several of them through the course of the year. It was her ministry. During the Thanksgiving season, she would awaken early on a Saturday, cook enough food for a small congregation, and then drive to the homes of those whom the Lord placed on her heart.

I TOOK THE LONG WAY HOME

I watched my mom fill a second pot with water and set it on a back burner. The sauce began to boil, with bursts of red popping up like popcorn, sprinkling the gas range.

"People have lost their minds," she said softly, stirring the sauce before covering it with a stainless-steel lid. "I don't know what's come of this world." She took a paper towel and wiped the droplets on the stove. "You think I don't know? I know. This boy's gonna tell you he loves you. And you know why? Because he wants to have his way with you. He doesn't love you."

"Yes, he does," I said.

The water in the pot on the back burner started to bubble. As she dumped a box of rigatoni into it, her thick eyebrows rose into the steam-drenched strands of hair on her forehead. "Is that what he told you?"

I shrugged. "Yeah."

She backed me into the counter with her intense glare. Her face moved close to mine and her eyes squinted. "I knew it," she exclaimed as if she'd caught me in the crime of the century. "You see him when you're visiting A'nanni. You tell us you're sleeping over at her house and then you go see him, don't you?"

"No," I cried out.

"I can see it in your eyes. You're lying."

"I'm not."

"Look me in the eye and tell me you haven't seen him," she said, searching my face.

I wanted to lie, but I couldn't. Not right to Mom's face. Maybe if I told the truth, she'd show some compassion for me. She'd see that I really loved Steven. Maybe she'd cave in and let me see him.

Tears stung my eyes. I was tired of sneaking around, sneaking Steven in and out of my bedroom window. It was too much work, too many lies to keep track of. "Just once," I said. "I saw him one time."

Her mouth dropped open as she sucked in a mouthful of air. Devastation, shock, and rage exuded from her being without her saying a word.

I waited for the inevitable lecture, prepared to stand there in the kitchen for the rest of the morning, listening to Mom rant and rave at me about honoring my parents[xli] and living for Jesus.

But she said nothing.

I waited for her hand to strike my face. But she didn't. She just stood there, staring at me in silence, for several seconds. It was worse than any lecture.

I thought I detected tears in her eyes. I'd never seen her cry—except at church when the missionaries came.

"Mom?" I said. "Are you okay?"

She didn't answer, just turned back to the stove and lifted the lid on the pot.

"It was only once," I moaned.

"Sure." She dipped the long wooden spoon into the sauce and moved it methodically around the edges of the pan. She lifted it to her mouth and slurped in the sauce, then nodded in satisfaction. "Just right," she said under her breath. She recapped the pot and stirred the rigatoni. Then she set the spoon on the range and wiped her hands on the sides of her stained apron.

Finally, she turned and looked at me, her eyes red and puffy. "All this time...I thought I could trust you."

"You can," I insisted.

"No," she said with a half-hearted smile. "You've changed. That boy's got you all twisted. He's got you lying to your own mother and father."

"He never made me lie."

"And you defend him? This boy means so much that you'd jeopardize your parents' trust?"

I couldn't say anything. I just stood there, overcome by the heaviness of being caught.

"It's a sad day," she said, shaking her head. "A sad day."

My eyes searched hers. "I'll never see him again. I promise."

"You already made that promise."

"I really mean it now. I won't see him anymore."

"Until he calls and tells you he can't live without you, or one of his other stupid lines."

I lowered my head.

"Just stay away from him, you hear me?"

"I am away from him. I'm all the way out here in the middle of nowhere and he's in the city."

"And no more going to see A'nanni. That ends right now. I want you here where we can keep an eye on you."

My head shot up. "What?"

"You heard me."

"But I won't see him anymore, I promise."

"I'm through with your promises. We can't trust you."

"Yes, you can!"

She folded her arms across her chest. "As long as you keep lying to me, you won't be allowed out of this house."

"I'm sorry, Mom; I really am."

She stared at me, her eyes misty. "Sorry isn't good enough anymore."

What? Never in my life had my mom not accepted an apology from me.

"That phone's coming out of your room too."

"What?" The phone was my lifeline to the outside world, my connection to Steven. "You can't take away my phone!"

"Oh, yes I can.

"You wouldn't."

"I will. And no more locks on those doors in your room."

"You can't do that!" I shrieked.

"Watch me." She began rinsing the cutting board in the sink. "For all I know you'll have that boy crawling in your window," she muttered.

I balked. "Like I would ever do that."

"Desperate people do desperate things." She scrubbed the wood with a sponge.

"This is so unfair!" I pounded my fist on the counter. "What about my privacy?"

"You'll need to earn that back."

"I said I was sorry. What more do you want from me?"

"I want my daughter back. The God-fearing daughter I raised."

I rolled my eyes, my blood boiling over like Mom's pasta sauce.

"All this time I've been defending you," she said, her voice cracking. "Telling your father you would never sneak around, that you'd never disobey us. Well, you proved me wrong."

"It was just once," I yelled.

She stopped the water and turned back to her pots on the stove. "Stephanie," she said softly, "you have your whole life ahead of you. High school. College. Don't let this guy fool you into thinking you're in love. You'll end up throwing your life away over foolishness. Save yourself for a nice Christian boy."

She faced me. "God has your husband already picked out for you. I've been praying for him since you were a little girl. Don't give yourself to some bozo who's already been with other girls. You're better than that. God made you special. You deserve someone who loves Jesus with all his heart, someone who's going to love you forever."

I'd heard this speech a million times. "You're not really taking the locks off my door, are you?"

"Yes."

I exhaled slowly. "For how long?"

"I don't know."

I scooped a handful of onion scraps into my palm and tossed them into the wastebasket under the sink. "You won't tell Daddy, will you?"

"Of course I'll tell your father. I don't keep secrets from my husband."

"But Mom!"

"Don't 'But Mom' me. You made this mess."

"He'll kill me!"

"You should have thought about that before you lied to us."

I felt my life crumbling in front of me. "He'll never let me out of the house again!"

"Whatever it takes to keep you away from that boy." She resumed her stirring.

"I can't do anything in this family," I screamed. "I can't even breathe without permission. I marched toward my room. "I feel like a prisoner!"

"You'll thank us someday," she called out.

"Whatever." I slammed the bedroom door behind me.

12   Losing Stephanie

After Mom informed Dad that I'd admitted to seeing Steven, the two of them combined forces and came up with an exhaustive punishment: three weeks of grounding, the confiscation of my bedroom phone, a cut in allowance, and the removal of the locks on my bedroom doors. When I huffed and puffed about him unscrewing the knobs, Dad even threatened to detach my bedroom doors, to ensure Mom had easy access to my room at all times. My parents had forged an all-out attack on my social life, making having a boyfriend nearly impossible.

Steven quickly grew tired of not seeing or hearing from me. The only times I could talk with him were before and after school on a pay phone in the hallway outside the principal's office. Hardly suitable for intimate conversations.

As the weeks of my grounding passed, my greatest fear came to fruition: A'nanni reported seeing Steven with another girl on at least three occasions. When I questioned him, he denied knowing anything about the brunette with the canary yellow jacket.

To prove he didn't have another girl, Steven invited me to attend his friend Kevin's eighteenth birthday party. My month of restriction would be over by then, and after the way I'd sulked around the house for three weeks, I figured my parents might not mind an excuse to get me out of the house. Besides, it was Christmas season; I hoped they might even feel bad for me.

Regardless of what they would or wouldn't let me do, I told Steven I'd get there somehow.

A'nanni's father bought us tickets to see A Christmas Carol at a theatre in Philadelphia the same night of the party. The tickets were for a late show, from eight to ten PM. I figured I could go to Steven's friend's party after that.

Selling Mom and Dad on going to the theater wasn't as easy as I'd thought it would be. They needed all the details. What kind of show? What time would it start? What time would it end? Who would accompany us? Why did I want to go? Finally, after I answered all their questions, Dad called A'nanni's father. He confirmed every detail. After Dad conferred with Mom, they announced that they would allow me to go—under one condition: I was not to have any contact with Steven.

I looked my father square in the eye. "I will not see or talk to Steven. Absolutely not."

Dad nodded. After weeks of watching me mope around the house, apologizing repeatedly for what I did, he would try to trust me again. "Everyone deserves grace," he said.

Dad even agreed to let me sleep over A'nanni's dad's house. "I'll pick you up in the morning." He hugged me.

As I squeezed my father's waist, all I could think about was seeing Steven. But as my arms fell to my side and I walked to my bedroom, I wondered why I wasn't more excited. My stomach turned at the thought of the lie I'd concocted to see him. What kind of person had I become? Was Steven worth the lies? Why couldn't I say no to him?

I was right back where I started. Their punishment had just delayed my rebellion.

Steven planned to pick me up from A'nanni's after the show ended. When A'nanni's father, a 70-year-old Ethiopian man, who'd been divorced and alone for many years, locked himself in the basement with his brandy, muttering words like "stupid Americans," we knew we were in the clear to roam about the house and neighborhood with nary a peep of interest from the basement.

"What time is Steven coming?" A'nanni asked as I sat on a couch in her living room, nervously waiting his arrival.

"Eleven," I sighed, having felt so terribly all night about lying. "I'm not even sure that I want to see him."

"You should just break up with him once and for all," she advised me. "He's so not worth it."

Agreeing with her, I answered, "I think I will. Tonight. I just can't do this anymore. I can't keep lying."

"Just have fun tonight and then move on with your life. Move on before something bad happens."

I nodded my agreement, convinced that it was time to let go. Though I'd invested so much of myself in Steven and our relationship, the return on that investment was ill gained. "Just this one more night," I promised myself aloud.

Steven was dressed nicely when he came to the door, with a musky cologne and brand-new leather jacket. Seeing him for the first time in so long sparked a sense of elation that I hadn't expected. My heart raced.

"I missed you so much," he said with a smile, pulling me close to him for a hug.

Concealing my excitement, I elbowed him away from me, suddenly remembering how uneasy I'd felt about lying and sneaking out and how I was still moderately bothered by his denial of—and A'nanni's persuasion of—his alleged brunette friend.

"Don't have an attitude tonight," he groaned, attempting to pull me close to him again. "I haven't seen you in a month. Please just be nice." I rolled my eyes and let him peck my cheek with a kiss, wondering to myself if his lips had kissed anyone else's in the weeks we'd been apart.

Resolving to at least try to have fun, I cooperated and joined him in the car for the ride to Kevin's. Though he assured we'd have a "great time," I couldn't quell the anxiety that sat like a lump of dough in my stomach.

We headed to Kevin's parents' house, a three-story brownstone in an elite neighborhood of north Philadelphia. The house was decorated for the season, with blinking white lights lined across each of the outer windows. A large silver Christmas tree adorned with red bows and matching garland greeted us at the door. There were eight of us: three teenage couples and Kevin's parents.

We ate picky foods prepared by Kevin's mother and, as the night went on, my anxiety waned and I warmed to Steven. We laughed and hugged and slow danced to songs like "Always and Forever." It was like we were in our own little world again, like those days in the subway train—me and my Steven. Though I'd planned to end things with him, it was as if we had started all over, as if we were still in love.

By one AM, after we'd toasted to Kevin's eighteenth year, his mother began lowering the music and wrapping up any uneaten food. It was her way of letting us know that it was time to leave. "I better get back to A'nanni's," I told Steven.

"I want you to stay with *me*," he whined.

"I can't," I affirmed. "I told A'nanni I'd be back."

"My father's away this weekend. We'll have the house to ourselves."

"But I told my parents I would be at A'nanni's," I moaned. "I feel so terrible about lying."

"Just this one night," he pleaded, devising a plan of how I could stay at his house without anyone knowing, how he would drive me home in the morning hours before my dad arrived.

"I can't," I said, though the offer tempted me.

"Please?" He crinkled his face. "I won't ask you to lie anymore." He held my hands in his. "It's been so long since we've seen each other...and I don't when I'll see you again. Please just come with me."

Those persuasive eyes swayed me. Maybe I could just stay for one night.

But I determined that it would be the last night for sure. It had to be. This life of lies had grown too exhausting.

I had Steven drive me to A'nanni's to retrieve my clothes.

A'nanni was furious when I told her my plan. Mumbling something inaudible and then stomping around her house with obvious dissatisfaction, she handed me my overnight bad. Her angry eyes found mine and I could sense that she too had grown tired of the lies. "I thought you were supposed to end it with him."

"Just one more night," I promised her. "Then it's over."

"I hate him," she grunted. "You can do so much better. All he'll do is break your heart." I knew she was right. But in my ignorance and stubbornness, I thought I could control the situation in which I invested so much of my time and life and ultimately avoid heartbreak.

We arrived at Steven's house and he was on his best behavior: sweet and attentive and caring, whispering the most adoring promises—*I want to spend my life you; You're the only one for me; I can't live without you.* Everything I wanted to hear. He even asked if I'd marry him in ten years. "Soon as I'm out of law school," he said. It was the old Steven again, before the move to New Jersey, before the drinking and the alleged brunette. I remembered all the reasons I had fallen for him. Perhaps it was those very reasons that led to my impulsive decision that night.

Because that was the night I lost my virginity.

When I returned home from my night with Steven, the enormity of my decision settled in: I was no longer a virgin. The promise I'd made to my God and my parents was broken. There was no turning back. I not only betrayed my parents, I betrayed

God. I had done something that could never be undone. There was no going back. I had sinned.

I never wanted to see Steven again.

For the next week he called relentlessly but I refused to answer the phone.

One time Steven even asked my father if I was home. Dad told him I was unavailable.

"Why is that boy calling here?" my father demanded. "Did you see him last weekend?"

"No," I lied.

"I thought you told him not to call you anymore."

"I did tell him," I said mournfully. "I can't stop a person from calling."

The following Friday, I went to youth group and asked the pastor to pray with me. Without being specific, I told him I had done something for which I needed forgiveness. He obliged graciously. He prayed that the Lord would forgive me, but not only forgive me; reveal His power to me. He prayed that I would submit my life to Christ, for He had good plans for me, plans to prosper me and not to harm me.[xlii]

After that evening, I felt that I had indeed been forgiven. My burden of guilt was left at the foot of the Cross. I had a renewed energy. I even volunteered to accompany the youth group on a missions trip to Mexico—something I'd balked at just a few weeks earlier.

I told my parents the news as soon as I got home. They were ecstatic. The Word of God they had so carefully implanted in me was finally beginning to spring forth.

Only one concern still lingered in the pit of my stomach. Although God forgives sin, I knew we're often left to deal with the consequences. I couldn't help but wonder what consequence I would have to endure.

13 It Only Takes Once

Three months passed. Steven stopped calling and my life went on as usual. There was only one thing missing: *my period*.

"I'm not sure," I said to A'nanni over the phone one afternoon after school, "because I never really keep track, but I think my period's late."

"You're kidding."

I twirled my fingers around the knotted phone cord.

"No. I haven't gotten it in awhile."

"When did you last do *it*?" she asked.

"Just that one time."

"That was like three months ago."

"I know. Should I be freaking out?"

"No. Not yet." She paused. "Do you feel any different?"

"I've been peeing a lot. Like every five minutes."

"I think that's a sign."

"Do you really think—"

"No. No way. You can't get pregnant on the first time."

"Please don't say that word. Just say P."

"Okay."

I curled up on the floor in a corner of my bedroom, trembling.

"Did you tell Steven you might be…P?"

"No. I haven't talked to him. I hate him."

"What will you do if you are?"

"I don't even want to think about it."

"Maybe your body's just changing. I hear it takes a while for your body to get adjusted to…you know, *doing it*. For the first time."

"You think?"

"Why don't you take a test?"

"I'd rather not know."

"But if you are, you'd have to do something about it. Soon."

"Like what?"

"You know."

Surely she wasn't suggesting… "Are you crazy?"

"No one would ever know."

"I would know. And God would."

"But your parents wouldn't."

"I could never do that."

"My sister's friend had one. She said it wasn't so bad. I don't even think you have to pay for it."

"I'd rather die."

"So you would have the baby?"

"Don't say that out loud," I screeched. "What if someone hears you?"

She apologized. "So," she whispered, "would you have it?"

"No. I would kill myself."

"Don't say that."

"Seriously. My dad would have to quit his job. I'd rather just be dead."

"I still think you should take a test. At least you'll know for sure."

"And then what?"

"I don't know."

"I'm really scared," I murmured.

"Why don't you talk to my sister? Remember when she thought she was?"

"I forgot about that. Is she home?"

"Yeah, hold on."

My heart pounded as I heard A'nanni hand the phone to her older sister.

"Hey, Steph," Sehai said. "How are you?"

"Not good," I replied.

"What's wrong?"

"I think I might be...P."

"What's P?"

"You know."

"Pregnant?"

"Please don't say that out loud."

"Sorry," she said, whispering.

"I did it with Steven in December, and I haven't had my period since."

"Did you use protection?"

"No."

"Did you take a test?"

"No. But I don't think I am. We only did it once."

"Doesn't matter. It only takes once."

"What?" My heart sank.

"Yep. Once is all it takes."

"So what if I am?" I felt myself coming apart. "What am I going to do?"

"You could have it taken care of. It's confidential. Your parents would never have to know. You could just go on with your life as if nothing happened."

"I could never do that."

"Everybody says that. Until they find out they're pregnant."

"Not me. I can't."

"Well, you should definitely take a test."

"Where do I get one?"

"Any drugstore. I can get one for you and you can come over after school tomorrow. At least A'nanni and I could be with you when you take it."

I agreed.

"Does Steven know?" Sehai asked.

"Not yet."

"He needs to know. You should call him."

"I will," I grunted, even though he was the last person I wanted to talk to.

"Don't worry. This kind of thing happens all the time. Tomorrow we'll know for sure."

"Thanks for talking to me. I'll see you tomorrow."

I hung up, took a deep breath, and called Steven.

He answered on the fist ring.

"Hey," I said.

"Steph." He sounded surprised. "Where you been? I called you like a hundred times."

"I know."

"I miss you. I want to see you."

"I don't want to see you," I said firmly.

"I love you, Steph."

"I really don't care."

"When can I see you? I need to see you. Why don't you come to the city after school tomorrow?"

"I'm going to, but not to be with you."

"Then who?" he growled. "Are you with someone else now? Is that why you haven't called?"

"No," I said, wishing I could hang up and never hear his voice again. "I'm going to A'nanni's. We have something to do. It's why I called."

I took a long, nervous breath.

"Steven, my period is late."

He was silent for a moment. "What?" he stammered.

"You heard me," I charged.

"What do you mean? *How* late?"

"Like three months."

"Three months? Are you kidding me?"

"This is not something I'd joke about."

"And you're just telling me this now?"

"I was hoping it would come. But it hasn't."

Neither of us said a word for a long time.

"So what's this mean?" he finally asked.

"I don't know," I whisper-screeched. "But I'm scared to death."

"I'm scared too."

"A'nanni and Sehai think I should take a test," I said. "I'm going over there tomorrow."

"You told A'nanni and her sister before telling me?"

"I didn't know what else to do."

Another long silence followed as I sat curled in a corner of my dark bedroom. I couldn't imagine what was going through his mind. A high school senior, top of his class, on his way to Penn State University to major in criminal justice. Just shy of his eighteenth birthday, and hit with the news that he may become a father.

"You okay?" he asked.

"No," I said, my lips quivering. "Please say something."

"I don't know what to say."

"Sehai said she would pick up the test for me. I'm supposed to meet her after school to take it."

"Why don't you cut school with me tomorrow? We'll take the test together. A'nanni and Sehai don't need to be involved."

"I can't cut school."

"Yes you can."

"I don't want to be with you!"

"This is not about what you want," he shrieked back. "I deserve to know whether or not you're pregnant."

Fine, I thought without saying anything.

"I'll pick you up in the morning."

My silence was as much an agreement as any words.

"Meet me in the back of the school parking lot," he said. "We'll talk then."

"Fine," I murmured.

"Steph?" He paused. "I'm sorry."

"I have to go." I hung up.

The next morning I crouched behind several parked cars in the school parking lot and waited for Steven.

My eyes squinted toward the roadway as I watched for his car. Random cars driven by careless seniors rumbled into the lot. One car's fender was so low it scraped the cement driveway with a loud thump. Rap music leaked from the windows as students shuffled out, cursing and yelping, making their grand entrance—fashionably late for school.

I sighed as the crooked metal doors on the side of the building shut off the last vestige of noise. Steven was now forty-five minutes late. I made up my mind that if he didn't show up in the next five minutes I would just go to school.

Five more minutes passed and still no sign of Steven. I decided to wait another two. Maybe he was stuck in traffic. *He'd better be.* I needed to know as soon as possible if I was pregnant or not. I didn't want to wait until after school, when Sehai could do this with me.

Twenty cars passed, and still no Steven.

I started to cry.

After several minutes of sobbing, I composed myself. I wiped my nose and cheeks with my sleeve, collected my book bag and purse, and stood. I decided I could no longer wait for him.

Just then I heard footsteps crunching on the gravel nearby.

"Forget this stupid school," a familiar voice uttered. I turned and saw one of the few friends I made at my new school: Laura Bennett, school outcast, strutting across the parking lot with her fists balled at her side and her eyes narrowed. Short and round with long permed hair tucked beneath a black headband, she was a loner and a hothead. She also had a severe case of *senioritis.*

Like me, Laura didn't have many friends at school. She was abrasive and had stated on many occasions that she was simply not a good fit for a school full of cozy suburbanite kids. So she rarely came to school. When she did come, the teachers found some reason to send her home for the day. Today was no doubt one of the days.

As she barreled forth, I smiled for the first time all morning. "Laura!" I shouted.

She stopped in her tracks, looked at me curiously, and smiled. "Hey, what're you doin' out here?"

I ran over to her, dragging my book bag and purse on the gravel, and collapsed into her arms.

"What's wrong?" she asked.

"I was supposed to cut school with my boyfriend—ex-boyfriend—but he never came." My eyes filled with tears again.

Framing my face with her hands, she asked, "You ain't gonna cry, are you?" I stifled a snivel. "Forget him. He's a loser. He ain't worth your time if he's gonna stand you up."

"But...you...don't...understand," I managed to get out between sobs.

"What don't I understand? That he's a jerk?"

I shook my head. "I think I'm...pregnant."

Her face turned white. "Oh, boy." She cradled my head in her chest as I wept like a toddler who'd lost her mother in a crowded mall.

"Where's the jerk live?"

"Philly," I answered, my voice raspy and muffled.

"Follow me," she commanded. "Let's go get him."

14   The Decision

I hadn't seen Steven since *the night*, and I didn't want to get him—I wanted to get away from him.

"Think the jerk's at school?" Laura probed.

"I doubt it. Maybe he's on his way to our school and—"

"He ain't on his way," she interjected. "He don't care about you. If he did, he wouldn't have gotten you pregnant." She waved her finger at me. "And he sure as heck wouldn't have left you in some parking lot."

She was right. Steven had left me to deal with this situation alone.

"If you don't beat the boy up, I will."

We made it to downtown Philly in twenty minutes. Laura drove like a NASCAR racer, her eyes gleaming with an audacious determination.

We reached the street on which he lived and found Steven by his car, watching his neighbor, Mikey, a short, gangly guy with wiry hair and pierced ears, tinker under the hood. At the sound of Laura's car, the guys craned their necks. Steven gawked, then a small grin crept out of the corner of his mouth when he realized it was me.

"That's him," I told Laura, "the taller one."

"He's cute," she admitted. "The cute ones are always the biggest jerks."

Laura stopped her car next to Steven's. He walked to the passenger side.

I rolled down the window. "What happened to you?"

"Car wouldn't start. Mikey gave me a jump; he's making sure everything's okay now."

"Whatever," I said, crossing my arms.

"What's with the attitude?" he challenged. "Did you think I would just leave you out there?"

"What else would she think?" Laura yelled over.

"Who are you?"

"Your girl's friend." They exchanged unpleasant looks.

"Well, you need to mind your own business," he barked.

"And you need to take care of your business."

"You don't even know me." He shook his head at Mikey, who was lowering the hood of the car. Then he turned back to me. "Come out," he said, opening the car door. "I need to talk to you."

"I can't." I closed the door.

"If you're not gonna talk to me, why did you come?"

Leaning across my lap, Laura yelled, "She came to watch me beat you up!"

Steven ignored her comment. Agitated, he balled his fists and swore under his breath. "Come on, Steph."

"No. I can't leave my friend."

He dug into his pocket and tossed a crinkled twenty-dollar bill through the window. It landed in the cup holder between the two front seats. "Go get some gas. I'll get her home."

"Will you be okay?" Laura asked, touching my hand. I nodded. Glaring at Steven, she grabbed the money and stuffed it into the pocket of her jeans.

Restraining a grin, Steven opened the car door again and helped me out. I exchanged a last look with Laura, assuring her that I would be okay.

"Call me later."

I promised I would, then watched her car rattle up the street.

Steven thanked Mikey for his work on the car and promised he would catch up with him later.

After Mikey left, Steven took my hand and led me into the house. As soon as the door shut behind us, he hugged me. His body was warm and welcoming. While we embraced, I thought that between our bodies could be a tiny child, our offspring, nuzzled in my womb. I burst into tears.

"It'll be okay," he said, consoling me. "Even if you are...you know...there's a way out. Don't worry. I have the money. I'll go with you, do whatever you need me to do."

His words cut through me like a knife. Before we even knew for sure, he had made up his mind how this would end: in death.

I pushed him away. "I can't do that."

"Yes, you can." He pulled me close to him. "You know neither of us is ready for a kid."

I pushed him further away. "I'd rather give it up for adoption."

"No, no. No adoption."

"I'll do what I want," I told him.

"Steph, we'll make the decision together. Based on what's best for both of us, okay?"

"I'm not having an abortion. I don't care what you say."

"We don't even know for sure yet." He picked up a small plastic bag from underneath one of the couch cushions. "I bought a test last night." He reached in the bag and pulled out a red-and-white box that read *Home Pregnancy Test.*

Looking at the box that would soon determine my destiny, I considered both possible outcomes. A negative result would be the ideal scenario. It would rid me of Steven. Life would go on as normal for the most part. But I didn't need a test to know that some crazy things were going on in my body. The fluttering I felt in my stomach at nighttime; the cravings; abnormal sluggishness; tenderness in my breasts; swelling in my lower belly; backaches. As much as I wanted to believe nothing was happening, I knew I had to be pregnant.

A sudden thrust of terror swept through my body. "I'm not taking it," I announced.

"You have to. If you don't find out soon, it'll be too late."

"I'll take it with A'nanni and Sehai at their house."

"No. I want you to take it here, now, so I know you're not lying."

"Lying?" I squealed. "You think I would lie about this?"

"Then take the test. What are you afraid of?"

"I'm afraid of the truth."

"Well, fear won't solve anything."

I snatched the box from his hands and marched upstairs. He followed close behind me, his shoulders and arms bumping my legs as I climbed the steps. When I reached the bathroom, I slammed the door behind me and locked it.

"Let me in," he demanded from the hallway. "I wanna see with my own eyes."

"You'll have to wait."

I stared at the small, unfamiliar contraption. I studied the instructions, which were written in three "easy to follow" steps. The third step indicated that I would need to wait two to three minutes for the results to appear (a red plus or minus sign). With Steven twisting the doorknob every three seconds, I squatted over the toilet.

"Let me in, Steph, or I'll break in."

I ignored his threat.

I Took the Long Way Home

Finishing, I placed the contraption on the sink, sat on the edge of the bathtub, and waited.

Contrary to what the instructions promised, it took less than thirty seconds for a solid red plus sign to materialize.

It was true. I was going to have a baby.

Steven pounded on the door. "I'm coming in."

I sat quietly as he hammered his body against the door. With a deafening boom, he burst into the room. His gaze immediately shifted toward the sink, where the contraption lay. His face depressed of buoyancy at the sight of the red plus sign that had temporarily paralyzed me.

Looking at me, his shoulders collapsed. "What do we do?" He crouched beside me on the side of the bathtub, his knees against mine. I covered my face. He took my hands and held them, drawing my eyes toward his. "You know there's only one thing we can do."

"I'm not—" I began, pulling my hands from his grasp.

"I know you don't want to," he whispered. "But we're kids, Steph. We have our whole lives ahead of us. What do we know about being parents?"

I cringed at the thought that I would be forced into an abortion. It wasn't fair. This child hadn't asked to be born while its parents were still in high school. Who was I to choose whether he or she should live? Bad timing didn't seem reason enough to terminate the life of my own child. The whole idea seemed criminal.

"It's the only way," he said.

"I could never live with myself."

"But how could you tell your parents that you're pregnant? It would break their hearts."

His words silenced me. He was right. How would Dad tell the congregation that the pastor's daughter was pregnant? And what about our extended family? Out-of-wedlock pregnancies didn't happen in families like ours.

"No one will ever have to know." Steven squeezed my hand.

No one will ever know, I repeated to myself. We'll all just go about our lives as if nothing ever happened, as if a life had not been extinguished from existence.

"You don't want your family to go through all that." Steven stood, pulling me up with him. "It would kill them."

Knowing I had an abortion would kill them, I thought.

"It's the easiest way for everyone." He rested his hands on my shoulders.

Easy? A rush of anger raced through my body. "The only person this would be easy for is you!" I pushed his hands off my shoulders and bolted out of the room.

Steven reached for me as I charged through the doorway, but I pulled away and ran down the stairs. Leaving my book bag and purse behind, I pushed through the front door and darted onto the sidewalk. The cool March air smacked my face hard as I scurried down the street, holding my belly, which I knew now carried a baby.

I crossed several streets without paying any attention to where I was going. Nothing seemed to matter—not even the blasting car horns and cursing drivers behind me. I hoped one of them would hit me. At least then I wouldn't have to deal with the consequences of my sin.

I ran eight blocks until I reached A'nanni's house. It was almost eleven AM. If anyone was home, it would be Sehai.

Sweating and exhausted, I pressed the doorbell and waited.

A full minute passed. I pounded on the door and rang the bell again. Still nothing. Finally, I heard thumping from inside the house, like someone shuffling down the stairs. Sehai swung open the door and greeted me with a toothbrush in her mouth and toothpaste dripping from her bottom lip. "Oh, my gosh," she gurgled, swallowing and yanking the toothbrush out of her mouth. "Are you okay? What happened?"

"I took...the test."

Sehai escorted me into the living room, where I collapsed on the couch, my hands and feet throbbing.

"I thought you were taking it with us...here...later."

I shook my head. "Took it. With Steven," I explained between sobs.

Sitting beside me on the couch, she rested her hand on my knee. "It was positive, wasn't it?"

I nodded as tears streamed from my eyes.

"Maybe it was wrong."

It wasn't. The only thing wrong was the decision I'd made to have sex with Steven.

The doorbell rang. Sehai shot an alarmed gaze at me. "Do you think that's Steven?"

I closed my eyes. I was so sure it was.

Looking out the window, she nodded. "Should I let him in?"

I TOOK THE LONG WAY HOME

I shrugged.

She opened the door, letting him inside without a word. As he entered the living room, his gaze turned toward the couch where I sat.

"Want to take a ride?" he asked.

Though he was the last person I wanted to be with, he was the only other person in the world who was in as much trouble as I was. Maybe the ride would do us both some good.

We drove in silence for at least two miles. I wished he would say something—anything to diffuse the awkwardness and uncertainty of the moment.

"I think we both know what we have to do," he finally said.

"I'm not having an abortion."

"Please just think about it." He sighed. "I'm going to college in five months. What kind of father can I be when I'm away? If we were ten years older, even five years. But not now. I'm not ready."

"You think I want to be a mother? I want to have a normal life too."

"That's all the more reason not to have it." He pounded his hands on the steering wheel.

I couldn't believe the guy who'd said he would love me forever would ask me to do such a thing.

I recalled a Psalm I'd learned as a little girl, where David described how fearfully and wonderfully we are made.[xliii] I thought of the small baby inside my belly. Despite the circumstances, God knew all about him or her already. He would stitch this child together in my womb[xliv] just as He'd stitched me and knew every hair on my head.[xlv]

"Why aren't you saying anything?" Steven pulled me from my thoughts.

"Because there's nothing left to say," I said. "I'm having this baby."

15 Not the Pastor's Daughter

Sehai drove me home later that afternoon.

Without saying much to Mom, Dad, or Michael, I excused myself from dinner, claiming I felt ill. Dad asked if I wanted prayer. I declined.

I shut myself in my bedroom and prayed alone. I cried out desperately to God in repentance for what I had done. I begged for forgiveness and asked in vain that I would wake up the next morning and no longer be pregnant. I hoped that somehow God would find mercy on me and just make everything the way it was before Steven came along, before I chose to lie and rebel.

But like I had heard Dad say so many times from the pulpit, I had to deal with the consequence of my sin.

I didn't hear from Steven the following day, nor in the days to follow. It was clear I'd have to deal with the situation on my own.

As time passed, I constructed various plans in my mind that would somehow prevent my parents from ever knowing I was pregnant. I contacted a girlfriend of mine, who lived in New York City, hoping I could run away to her house, have the baby, and then give it up for adoption. When her mother said, "No way," I tried a friend of mine who'd moved to Ohio. She cried hysterically after I told her about the situation. I asked A'nanni and asked if she thought her father would notice if I moved into his garage for three to four months. She said that seemed unlikely.

My options were waning. Apart from running away for good or faking my own death, I would eventually have to tell my parents. It was only a matter of time.

The days turned into weeks as my mind filled with worry and fear. I was sure Steven had moved on to his next conquest. I could picture him holding hands with a pretty brunette, telling her things like *I love you* and *I can't live without you* just as he'd told me.

I fell into a deep depression. I ate very little and talked only when necessary. While other girls at school talked about their summer vacation plans, I remained quiet. As they talked about the cute outfits they'd bought for nights on the boardwalk, I tugged at my oversized T-shirt that I wore to conceal the belly that had popped out against my will. When they talked about the end-of-the-year tournaments for softball and soccer and track, I was reminded of the all the things I would miss.

In attempt to conceal my condition from my parents for as long as possible, I did my best to act normal at home. But people outside my family started bombarding me with questions. My track coach asked why I suddenly quit the team. My boss asked why I needed to sit after four hours of standing at the register of his fast-food restaurant. My teachers asked why I fell asleep during classes.

Eventually, Mom and Dad began questioning my drastic change in behavior as well. "Why don't you talk to us anymore? Why aren't you eating?" I told them I just wasn't hungry or talkative. I didn't feel like smiling. I didn't care if my clothes were dirty. I didn't care about anything anymore. Nothing seemed to matter.

When I was six months pregnant, I had to get a passport to go to Mexico on our church missions trip. I would be in my third trimester at the time of the trip and I didn't think I could smuggle a nine-month-pregnant belly into Mexico without being noticed. I knew it was time to tell Mom and Dad.

Before I did, I called Steven. I wanted to let him know that I was going to tell my parents. Then maybe he would realize that the situation hadn't disappeared.

When he answered the phone, I didn't even say hello. I just blurted, "I'm telling my parents today."

He was quiet for a moment. I wished he would have at least said hello or asked how I was doing. Instead he asked, "What do you want me to do about it?"

His gruff, careless response triggered the emotional time bomb I'd kept bottled up for six months. I slammed down the receiver, flopped down on my bed, and sobbed. Just then I heard the front door shut. Dad came into my room and knelt beside me, looking anxious and worried. "Steph, are you okay? Why are you crying? What is it?"

"I want to die!" I screamed.

"Why? What happened?" His voice was anxious.

"Something terrible."

"Please tell me what's wrong. I want to help you."

"I can't. I can't tell anyone."

125

"Did someone make you do something you didn't want to do? Are you in trouble?"

I didn't answer him. I couldn't speak.

Then he asked a question I never thought I'd hear come out of my father's mouth. "Is your period late?"

I choked back tears and whispered, "Yes."

"How late?"

"A couple of months," I said.

"Are you pregnant?"

"I took a test," I moaned. "It was positive."

"Are you sure?"

"Yes."

He sat there quietly for several seconds. Then he stood and shuffled out the door. I heard his footsteps go up the stairs. I heard his bedroom door close. Then I heard the most horrible cries of agony I've ever heard from any human being.

As Dad's howls of sorrow reverberated through our house, I threw clothes in a bag. Stumbling through tears that nearly blinded me, I dumped the little money I had, seventy-eight dollars, into a purse and bolted out the front door.

I got about a half mile from my house before Dad pulled up beside me on the street. "Get in the car," he said calmly.

"I don't want to."

"Please."

I turned to look at him. His tears had dried, and his expression revealed a man who held firmly to the grace God gave him to get through any storm life rolled his way.

Reluctantly, I drifted into the passenger seat, my head hung low.

On the ride back, he said only one thing, "Steven?"

I nodded without looking at him.

When we arrived home, I rushed to my room and found Mom there, sitting on my bed. Without a word, she stood, grabbed me by the sleeve, and pulled me toward her. She lifted my shirt and inspected my belly, poking it with her forefinger. "Yep," she said, shaking her head, "you're pregnant." She sat back on the bed.

Dad came in. He paced from the door to the window of my room, stepping over clothes and books strewn across the floor. "There's a Christian home for girls in north Jersey," he said quietly, his words broken with emotion. "You'll stay there until you have the baby." His voice cracked with a bitter sadness.

I Took the Long Way Home

"Then you'll give the baby up for adoption." He paced the room one more time, then exited.

"I knew it," Mom said. "I told you that boy wouldn't stop until he had you."

"What do I do now?" I asked. "What can I do to fix this?"

"Nothing," she said. "Does that boy's family know?"

"No."

"Good. We'll tell them when we're ready."

The following day my parents took me to the gynecologist. I had never gone but had heard horror stories from friends about stirrups, a metal contraption squeezed into the vagina, and long, oversized cotton swabs. It all sounded inhumane and made me sick with fear.

The exterior of the building looked like an old house converted into office space. It was lined with bland yellow siding and maroon trim that matched the window shutters. Conversely, the interior was inviting, with a spacious reception area and soft music playing from speakers protruding from the dropped ceiling panels. The rugs were a rich navy blue with green polka-dots, and the temperature was comfortable. Several chairs were arranged around a table covered with women's magazines. Two pregnant women sat at opposite corners of the table, one with her nose in *Parenting* magazine and the other flipping through pages of a daily planner. Both wore wedding bands—an unpleasant reminder that no husband waited at home for me.

Dad approached the front desk. "Cavelli," he said quietly. "We have a 9:30 appointment."

Mom and I took chairs while Dad checked us in. After we filled out all the paperwork, the receptionist told us it would be just a few minutes before I would be seen. Dad paced from where Mom and I sat to the wall.

After a few minutes, a nurse emerged from the doorway and introduced herself as Anna. No more than forty years old, she had short blonde hair in a cute bob. She wore pale blue scrubs with bright white clogs. "Please follow me," she said to my parents. "We can talk in a more private area."

She led us down a short, narrow corridor to an examination room. "How are you both?" she asked my parents sympathetically as we entered the sterile, spacious waiting room, equipped with chairs, a TV and a medical scale. Mom said nothing; Dad shrugged. Anna looked at me for a brief moment, then spoke to my parents as if I wasn't standing right there beside them. Dad answered all her questions. Mom just stared at the woman. She looked tired. As if she'd been up all night. Hurt. As if all the dreams she'd had for me were slipping away. Lost. As if she didn't know how our family had gotten into to this place. "You both can wait here while we examine her," Anna told my parents.

The nurse finally addressed me. Sternly. "You'll need to follow me."

I walked behind her as she filed down a long, carpeted hallway to the last room on the left. "This is where we'll conduct your exam."

The room was cold and uncarpeted, and smelled of medication and disinfectant. After Anna weighed me and measured my height, she asked several personal questions about my sexual activity. The answers were short and concise: one person, one time.

She scribbled on a sheet of paper fastened to a manila folder and then handed me what looked like a paper tablecloth, which she called a gown, and ordered me to undress.

"All the way?" I asked in horror.

She nodded, then gave me a charitable look of regret and concern.

After she left, I tried to remain calm as I changed into the stiff paper wrapper.

Several minutes later, I heard a loud thump on the door. "Ready for me?" asked a deep, barreling voice.

Before I could respond, the doctor, a grey-haired man with glasses and a goatee, glided into the room, shutting the door behind him. He held the manila folder that Anna had written in. He stood by the door for a long moment, his eyes moving across the pages within the folder. He let out a harsh sigh that I interpreted as being filled with disapproval toward the pregnant teen who had disobeyed God and her parents.

He looked up at me, introduced himself as Dr. Jefferson, and offered the same charitable look Anna had given me on her way out.

The exam was awkward and painful. It felt like my insides were being sliced with a knife.

When it was over, the doctor removed plastic gloves and washed his hands in the sink. He instructed me to dress and wait for Anna. "See you in a few minutes," he said on his way out.

I TOOK THE LONG WAY HOME

Anna arrived just as I had finished dressing. "Ready?"

I nodded and followed her back to the room in which my parents waited.

"She'll need an ultrasound," I heard the doctor tell my parents. "I'd like to send her to the hospital today. She's pretty far along. Six months."

Mom and Dad gasped. I couldn't even look at them. For six months I was living a lie and neither of them had a clue.

At the hospital, a young, enthusiastic nurse named Kimmie greeted me. "Look how beautiful you are!" she said with an overpowering smile. "You're glowing!" I instantly liked her.

Rubbing my belly, she asked, "Excited to hear your baby's heartbeat, Mom?"

Mom? I thought. Didn't she know I wasn't really going to be a mom? Apparently she didn't get the press release.

"I bet that baby's keeping you up at night." She winked. "Jumping and kicking like it was on a trampoline!"

It sure was. I wanted to tell her all about the changes I hadn't been able to share with anyone.

She instructed me to undress—this time only to my waist. I did so quickly while she waited just outside the room. "All ready for me?" she asked, reentering the room. After smearing my belly with a blue jelly-like substance, she retrieved a medical device that looked like a laser pointer and swirled it around the jelly. A loud sound, like the hoofbeats of a galloping horse, filled the room.

"What's that?" I asked.

"That's your baby's heartbeat."

Wow. I'd never imagined it would sound so clear.

Kimmie stared at the black-and-white screen that showed a small blob wiggling around like a floating lima bean.

"Is that the baby?" I asked.

"Sure is. Do you want to know the sex?"

I nodded.

"It's a boy."

I was carrying a little boy. Most women would turn to their husbands at that point and exchange a comforting grin at such great news. But not me. My excitement dissipated as I realized that I was hearing the heartbeat of the son I would never know.

When I returned home from a full day of doctors and check-ups, I decided to call Steven. I figured he should know that he would have a son. Besides, it wasn't fair that I had to go through this alone. He should have to endure at least some of the pain I did.

I called at seven that evening. When he didn't answer his own line, I called the house phone. His father answered.

"Is Steven home?"

"No," he said in broken English with a thick Italian accent. "He's at his girlfriend's house."

I swallowed hard. Just as I suspected, Steven had found himself a new love. While I was poked and scanned and smeared, he enjoyed a life of negligence. My temper burned.

"Please tell him that Stephanie called. You can also tell him I'll be having his son in September."

I expected the old man to be as irate as I was. Instead he just made a strange grunting noise.

"I guess Steven forgot to mention to you that he has a baby on the way."

His father still said nothing.

"Just thought I'd let you know," I said, my voice singing a tune of reckless release. Then I slammed the phone down with vengeful determination.

I called his mother next. A voicemail message informed me that she wasn't home. After the beep, I said calmly, "This is Stephanie Cavelli. I'm calling to let you know that I'm pregnant with Steven's baby, and I'm due in September." It all came out so quickly—too fast to recover. I paused, debating whether I should I say more. "I guess that's it," I said nonchalantly. "Good-bye."

I hung up with a liberating satisfaction.

I would wait for the aftermath.

Steven's mother called later that evening. My mother answered the phone and I listened on the extension.

She went on and on about how appalled she was. But she seemed more concerned that her son hadn't told her about the pregnancy than that he'd sired an illegitimate child. "It's so unlike him," she told my mother. "He's very responsible. He has a full academic scholarship to Penn State, you know. I can't imagine he would ever be involved in such an ordeal."

"Well, he can't be all that responsible," my mother said, "if he got my daughter pregnant."

"Excuse me?" she demanded.

I Took the Long Way Home

My father grabbed the phone from my mother and glared at her, holding his hand over the mouthpiece.

"Well, it's true," my mother muttered. "Her kid's a pig, and she talks about him like he's some kind of saint."

Dad apologized for Mom's comment, chatted with her for a few moments, then hung up.

"She wants to meet with us," Dad announced.

"Meet with us?" Mom asked. "For what?"

"She thinks we should talk about what's going to happen."

Great, I thought. As if I hadn't gone through enough humiliation already.

I figured Steven was even more reluctant about seeing my parents than I was about talking to his. I half expected him to call my folks and let them in on a few secrets of his own, like the fact that he'd slept over a dozen times without their knowledge, and about all the times I'd told them I was visiting A'nanni but was really with him. He had more on me than I had on him. But the evening of the meeting came without a word from him.

His stepfather's black Mercedes pulled into our driveway at 6:30. Steven emerged first, wearing knee-length denim shorts, a black pullover, and white Reeboks. His mother climbed out of the passenger seat, her thin, tanned legs stretching out to the paved driveway. The doctor came out last. He was average height, a few inches shy of six feet, and wore a three-piece business suit and a red power tie.

Steven's mother strutted to the door with her nose in the air, clutching her husband's hand. Steven sulked behind them, his gaze on the ground.

My father greeted the threesome at the door. "Hello. I'm Tony Cavelli."

"Roger Donato. This is my wife, Paula."

"Thanks for coming." The men exchanged handshakes while Paula offered a curt frown.

"Hello, Steven," Dad said, shaking his hand.

Steven mumbled, "Hi."

They all walked through the kitchen and into the living room, where my mother and I sat on a loveseat. The Donatos sat on the couch facing us. Steven took a chair in the corner, close to me. I refused to look at him.

Mom glared at Paula, her right eyebrow raised and her mouth curled. All of Christ's teachings about love and kindness appeared to have been zapped from her memory. She looked ready to start a battle at the slightest negative comment concerning her daughter.

Dad stood where he could watch us all at the same time. There he was, a pastor, counselor, and teacher, shepherd of God's church, preparing to discuss the details of his daughter's out-of-wedlock pregnancy with strangers. The fate of a child, his grandson, fathered by a boy who, before this night, he had never seen, would be determined in this meeting. Yet somehow, he maintained his composure.

"Stephanie is going to a home for pregnant girls in north Jersey. She'll stay there until the baby's born. Then the child will be put up for adoption."

"Oh, really?" Steven's mother asked. "I'm guessing this was decided without any input from my son?"

My mom leaned forward, clearly ready to launch a verbal missile. But Dad stopped her with a look. "We thought adoption would be best, not only for the baby, but for Stephanie and Steven as well. They're both kids, and neither is in a position to raise a child." Dad looked at the Donatos and then at Steven. "Unless you can think of a better idea that would benefit everyone involved."

Paula's head bobbled in an indignant swagger. "Once paternity is established, I'd be glad to offer my ideas."

The room froze in silence. All eyes focused on me. I shot a look at Steven, silently urging him to say something.

"Ma," he said quietly, "please."

"What?" she said. "It's a legitimate concern. You can't just take the girl's word for it."

"I told you—"

Before he could finish, Mom jumped to her feet and waved her finger in Paula's face, "How dare you! Your son's the one who should be questioned. He's the one who preyed on my virgin daughter!"

Paula's mouth dropped opened.

Dad motioned for Mom to sit. She didn't.

"Let's handle this diplomatically," Dad intervened. Looking at Steven, he asked, "Do you acknowledge that this is your child?"

Steven nodded.

"Do you have any doubt that it's yours?"

I Took the Long Way Home

"None." He shot a look at his mother, who pursed her lips in a conspicuous expression of surrender.

Mom's eyes narrowed at Paula as she finally backed into her seat: a silent warning that she'd better behave. But she didn't.

"In that case, I think my son should be deciding with Stephanie on what's best for *their* child."

It was a deliberate attack on my parents.

"Stephanie is sixteen," Dad said. "Not yet an adult. As her parents, we'll help her make the best decision. If Steven has any better ideas than adoption we'll certainly consider them."

All eyes shifted toward Steven.

He folded his arms on his lap and sighed. "I'm leaving the decision to Stephanie and her parents—" he began before his mother butted in.

"No he isn't."

"Yes. I am." He glared at her. "I'll support whatever decision they make."

Turning to me and my parents, he offered only his backing. "If you go through with the adoption, I'll support you. If you decide to keep him..." He shrugged. "Then I'll be a father and I promise to be there for him."

Inside, I cheered. At least he would cooperate.

Though the meeting began under the presupposition that Steven and I would determine the fate of our child, our opinions seemed to dissolve as four adults discussed the future of a child who didn't belong to any of them. I felt lifeless as I listened to words like *the child*, *adoption*, and *adoptive parents*.

Despite its unsettling beginning, the night ended amicably, the adults agreeing that adoption was indeed the best solution. "Do you accept this decision?" Dad asked us.

Steven and I exchanged looks.

"I guess." I shrugged.

"Whatever Steph wants." He sighed.

And just like that we verbally resigned as parents.

When the guests left, I followed my parents into the kitchen in a haze of confusion.

"Jesus," my mother said, staring up at the ceiling, "guide our steps. Direct us, Lord."

My father chimed in with his own plea. "We can do nothing without You, Lord. Give us the strength to get through this." His voice trailed off as he joined Mom for a hug.

Panting, as if trying not to cry, he then looked at me. "It'll be okay, Steph." He started to cry. "The Lord will work it all out."

The next evening, Dad informed Mom and I that he arranged an urgent meeting with the church board to share the news of my condition. As God's anointed shepherd over them, Dad's obligation was to model Christlike behavior, which meant honesty at all expense. Even the expense of his position.

Dad left shortly after 7 PM and didn't return until 10 PM.

Mom and I questioned him as soon as he entered. Still visibly distraught, he spoke in brief, concise sentences.

"All six men attended."

"They prayed with me."

"Wept with me."

"Promised they'd stand by us."

Mom and I sat silently as Dad took short, deep breaths, desperately trying to hold back tears.

"I'll need to tell the church this Sunday."

"The whole church?" Mom asked.

"Yes."

"From the pulpit?" I asked.

"Yes."

My abdomen contracted. The thought of my shame made known to the whole church sickened me. *The consequences continued.*

That Sunday, Dad announced from the pulpit that there would be a special meeting for church members following the service. I sank in my seat.

My father struggled through the service, preaching with distress and uneasiness. The man who'd led my family with grace and confidence since I was a child, a man normally brimming with the joy of God's Holy Spirit, was rigid and methodical.

As Dad commenced the benediction prayer at the end of the service, I hurried out the back door with Mom and Michael. We'd planned beforehand that no one in our family would be present when Dad made the dreadful announcement. We drove home in silence as if we were fleeing a hit-and-run.

When we pulled into the driveway of our house, Mom rushed inside and ran up to the master bedroom. The door slammed behind her. She didn't even look at me.

I didn't want to look at myself. It all seemed unreal. Our precious world was coming undone and there was nothing any of us could do to stop it.

When Dad came home later that afternoon, he knocked on my bedroom door. "Can I come in?" he asked, his voice hoarse and raspy.

Part of me thought he might never speak to me again. The other part wondered if, like Mom, he couldn't bear to look at me.

When I answered the door I saw a broken man. His red cheeks and bloodshot eyes evidenced tears that I knew nothing of. I could only assume that the hoarse voice that accompanied those tears was the product of more cries of agony on behalf of the daughter he would soon send off to have a baby at the age of sixteen.

I would learn much later in life that when Dad informed the church family of my condition from the pulpit, he said simply, "*My daughter is pregnant. Please pray for our family.*" He then left the pulpit and walked down the center aisle. Before passing the third row of silenced parishioners, he was surrounded by church family. They enclosed him for prayer. They knelt beside him on the floor of the church. They stayed with him all afternoon on the floor of the church, praying with him, weeping with him, bearing his burden as all families should.

Because of their support he was able to look at me wearily and say the last words I expected to hear. "I love you," he said to me, standing at the door. Though he'd said those words a million times, they meant so much at that moment.

"I'm so sorry, Dad."

"It's going to be okay," he assured as he'd done the night that Steven and his family came. "It's all going to be okay."

16   Sent Away

I left the next day for the girls' home.

Mom and Dad woke me at six AM to get dressed and ready.

As I packed a few final things into a suitcase, wishing I was going away to camp or vacation instead of a home for pregnant teens, my brother crept into my room. His hair was a thick, tangled mess. He wore oversized sweatpants and a wrinkled T-shirt. His usually pleasant face was filled with the alarming realization that he would soon be left to fend for himself in a world that had always been, in some sense, us against them (our parents). Never in his life had he lived without me.

"I can't believe you're leaving," he said as he sat beside my suitcase on the bed.

I couldn't believe it either.

"I'm worried about Mom and Dad," he murmured.

"So am I." His words doubled my burden. Not only was I carrying the weight of my own depression, but my parents' as well. This was all my fault. My labyrinth of lies and selfishness had caused this upheaval.

"Are you scared?" he asked.

I shrugged. I'd been so worried about my parents, I hadn't thought about myself. "I wish it would all just go away."

"It will," he assured me. "In a couple of months you'll be back to normal."

I sure hoped he was right.

After I finished packing, Michael carried my suitcase to the car, where Mom and Dad waited for me. His extra-long pants trailed behind him as he lugged the heavy load down the driveway. He hauled it into the trunk and said a quick good-bye to Mom and Dad. He declined our parents' offer to ride with us, saying he preferred to stay home. I couldn't blame him—I wish I had that option.

He hugged me from behind as if he were scared to make contact with my belly. "Miss you already," he said.

Not one for emotional good-byes, I shooed him off and promised I'd write. I climbed into the backseat of our family car and joined Mom and Dad for our journey.

The ride was excruciating. No music, no talking. Just silence. Leaving the surroundings of our home, we traveled across highways and off into small towns, down endless windy roads, with tall trees blocking any hint of sunlight. We passed cautionary signs of deer crossings and natural waterfalls jutting from great rocks. Reality settled in the further we voyaged: I was leaving home to have a baby. Everything inside me wanted to scream, "Don't make me go. Please!" But I knew there was no turning back.

An hour into the ride, Dad broke down into loud, sharp sobs. It was the first sound I'd heard since we left home. It felt out of place, like a sneeze in the middle of communion service or a cell phone ringing at a funeral. He buried his mouth in his shoulder to muffle his weeping then wiped his face with his hand.

Mom never flinched. Her loopy chestnut curls sat on the edge of her shoulders. Her round, black sunglasses hid any expression. If tears fell under those shades, no one would know it.

Almost two hours later, Dad pulled into the paved driveway of a sparsely decorated Victorian mansion—it had to be at least a hundred years old. If we'd arrived under any other circumstances, I'd have appreciated its beauty but there was no time for decorative admiration.

Dad exited the car first, then me, and finally Mom.

We followed a slate walkway around the house to an almost hidden main entrance. At the door, we were met by a large, white-haired woman wearing an ankle-length skirt tucked tightly between the bottom of her breasts and the top of her bulging gut. Bifocals dangled at the edge of her nose, and big pearl earrings dwarfed her small ears.

Beside her stood two caramel-colored Chihuahuas, tails wagging, looking up at us as if they had come to welcome the new girl. "Hellu," the woman said—not hello. "You must be the Cavellis." The woman called me by name and introduced herself as Ms. Wyman. "Not Mrs.," she quickly pointed out.

After Dad greeted her warmly, she escorted us through the foyer. My eyes bound from room to room as I surveyed what little I could from where we stood. Small, red-oak panels lined the ceiling, crowning burgundy papered walls. On the far right, just before the kitchen entrance, a great, snaking staircase led to the upper level.

Ms. Wyman led us through the house as her two pups, whom she introduced as Dutch and Thunder, tagged along. Each room had a name. Our first stop, the Media Room, was located on the main floor. With floor-to-ceiling bookcases containing encyclopedias, novels, and board games arranged neatly by height, three mismatched couches that looked like they'd been donated, a desk, and a baby grand piano, I suspected it was the most frequented room in the house.

The back of the room opened up to a screened-in porch that overlooked a lush backyard strewn with landscaped patches of grass and multicolored tulips. "This is where the girls spend most of their days," Ms. Wyman said. "I encourage them to read and use their God-given creativity."

From the Media Room, we entered the Night Room, located on the same floor. It was dreary and sparse, with dark brown paneled walls, a large TV mounted atop an oak credenza, and an old, plastic-covered couch that didn't look the least bit comfortable. Certainly not like our cozy couch at home.

From the Night Room, we entered the kitchen. It was bright and spacious, much larger than my parents' kitchen. A very pregnant girl sat at the table, reading a newspaper. Ms. Wyman introduced her as Tamika. Tamika, a tall African-American girl whose long legs stretched far under the table, wore a scarf around her hair. She half smiled at us over her glasses, then resumed reading.

"Tamika's been with us the longest," Ms. Wyman said.

Tamika forced a wave, visibly uncomfortable with the attention.

"Let's move on." Ms. Wyman ushered us back to the foyer, where she instructed Dad to retrieve my suitcase before we headed up the staircase. He did.

The long, creaky hallway smelled of fresh paint. "I just had the bedroom painted a few days ago," Ms. Wyman said as she opened a door at the far end of the hall. "I apologize if the odor still lingers. The girls have been sleeping downstairs the past few nights. I had them move back up here this morning."

We entered the bedroom. The air was laced with the smell of lotions and powder, and the very distinct fragrance of cocoa butter. The walls were pale blue, with a thick floral border that stretched from one corner to the other. She ran her hand against one of the walls. "Blue is a comfort color."

Four beds lined two of the walls. A tattered stuffed elephant lay on one bed; Mickey Mouse pillowcases hugged the pillows on another; an open suitcase sat beside the third bed. Ms. Wyman pointed to the bed with a pale blue comforter set and matching pillow. "That's your bed," she said. Dad propped my suitcase beside it.

We made our way back to the foyer. I knew it was time for Mom and Dad to return home—without me.

"I discourage long, emotional farewells," Ms. Wyman said. "I've found it's better just to get it over with quickly. Like removing a Band-Aid." She gave my parents a look that implied this was more of a policy than a suggestion.

Dad hugged me. He told me he loved me and promised to call first thing in the morning. Mom just waved and ran out, covering her face all the way to the car. I wondered if they would pull over at the nearest gas station to cry.

That night I met the girls. Denise, a fifteen-year-old half-black, half-Italian girl from the Bronx, was a few weeks further along than I was. Tiffany, a seventeen-year-old redhead from Paterson, New Jersey, was only four months pregnant. Tamika, the oldest, also from Paterson, looked like she could give birth at any moment. She had the biggest belly I'd ever seen. It seemed unreal, like a prop on a television show.

Within a day of my arrival I learned the rules and expectations. Everything about the girls' home was strict and orderly. Everything had a time and place, from assigned dinner seats and towel racks to closet space and bedtime. We cooked, cleaned, prayed, read, exercised, ate a regimented diet that excluded any sweets, and slept when we were told to. It felt like boot camp for pregnant teens. If it weren't for the other girls— the unexpected friends I made—my time there would have seemed like a jail sentence.

My favorite was Denise—maybe because she was closest in age to me. While the other two girls seemed capable of holding their own, Denise and I were young and naïve. She reminded me so much of A'nanni—her infectious laughter and her enthusiasm about the ordinary. "I'm going to do my hair today," she'd announce with such passion as if she'd decided to run for congress or something. She giggled constantly despite the grave circumstances surrounding her sojourn at the girls' home. I assumed nothing could quell the little girl inside her. She was honest and transparent. She even shared her darkest secret: that she wasn't positive about the identity of her child's father. "It's one of two guys. Either Tony or Lou. I hope it's Tony. He's so cute!" Though I'd only known her for such a short while, I concluded that only ditsy Denise could make a joke of something so seriously wrong.

Apart from church and food shopping, we rarely left the house. Tuesdays were the highlight of our week because that's when we accompanied Ms. Wyman to the grocery store.

The first time we made the trip, the girls took me into their confidence. When Ms. Wyman sent us off in pairs to get the items we needed, we split up and then met at the vending machine in the rear of the store, which sold chocolate. We acted like old ladies at a casino, popping quarters into the machine and watching the candy bars drop into our hands. We each stuffed two and three bars into our pockets or purses. I eagerly anticipated gobbling them up in our room that night, even if it made us all sick with indigestion.

Tamika was the resident beautician. Even with a stomach the size of a beach ball, she stood for hours at a time curling and crimping and straightening our hair. She even taught us how to pluck our eyebrows and give each other pedicures.

Occasionally, I actually felt normal. As if we were just four girls hanging out together for the summer. We reminisced about what our lives were like before we'd gotten into trouble.

We were all at the girls' home because we'd chosen adoption. Ms. Wyman would set up our hospital stays and link us with social workers who would connect us with adoptive parents. All of us had the same goal: to find good families for our babies so they could have the kind of lives we couldn't give them.

Tamika, the closest to delivering, had already chosen her adoptive parents, a well-to-do African-American couple from upstate New York. They were both in business and wanted nothing more than to have a child.

We rarely talked about our babies. Instead we focused on what we'd do after pregnancy. Tamika planned to enlist in the navy; Denise intended to try out for cheerleading and get a job; Tiffany anticipated getting her GED. As for me, I wanted to return to my school and graduate with honors, then get into a good college and move on with life. And stay away from Steven.

Mom and Dad visited almost every weekend. Sometimes they brought balloons or small gifts. When I told Mom that Ms. Wyman wouldn't let us have candy, she muttered, "That's ridiculous." So when she visited she always brought a bag of my favorite candies (Skittles) and chocolates (M&Ms)—enough for me and the girls. My roommates loved her for it.

Mom also sent letters and cards—sometimes three in one day. All of us girls waited for the mailman to arrive at noon, each of us hoping for cards or letters or pictures. But almost all of the mail was for me. Mom had the whole church writing to me. I got cards from people I didn't even know, each with a message that someone was praying for and thinking of me. Mom's cards reminded me how special I was and that the Lord still had a wonderful plan for my life. She sent Scriptures and lollipops and sticks of gum.

Steven called the house almost daily. Our conversations were brief and uneventful.

"What are you doing?" he'd ask.

"Nothing."

"How are you feeling?"

"Fine."

I knew he only called because he felt obligated to. Or perhaps his mother had suggested it.

Finally I asked him to stop calling. "It's pointless," I said.

"I'd at least like to know how you're doing."

"I'm fine," I assured. "I'll call you when I'm in labor."

Apart from phone calls and weekly outings to the doctor and the grocery store, life at the girls' home was routine and mundane. We all just waited for the inevitable: labor.

Then, one day, while we were gathered around the dinner table eating breaded chicken, sliced potatoes, and corn on the cob, Tamika set her fork down, clutched her stomach, and announced that her water had broken.

"Oh my goodness!" Denise cried. "Are you wet?"

"Hush," Ms. Wyman commanded. "Can you get up?" she asked Tamika.

She nodded and stood, revealing a soaked seat cushion.

"Oh my goodness, oh my goodness!" Denise moaned as if it was her water that had broken.

"That's enough!" Ms. Wyman yelled, startling Denise to settle down. She then barked orders. "Tiffany, you're in charge of cleanup. Denise, you have dish duty. Stephanie, gather Tamika's things and set them in the foyer for me. Be sure you pack her regular clothes."

Turning to Tamika, she said, "We need to get to the hospital. Now. Can you make it to the van?"

Tamika nodded.

Ms. Wyman called a neighbor and asked if she'd sit with Denise, Tiffany, and me while she went to the hospital. As she helped Tamika to the van, the rest of us peeked through a curtain in the Media Room.

"I'm so scared for her," Denise groaned.

"What are you scared about?" Tiffany asked. "You're next."

"But I don't want to have a baby."

"Shoulda thought of that before you got knocked up," Tiffany joked, although Denise wasn't laughing.

"I'm so scared," Denise mumbled again.

Watching Ms. Wyman peel out down the road, I felt pretty scared myself.

The following morning, Ms. Wyman called to tell us that Tamika had delivered a baby boy. She'd named him Blake. Ms. Wyman forbade the rest of us to go visit her. "She's not in any condition to see people." So instead of visiting, Denise and I sneaked to a payphone and called her hospital room. Tamika gave us the whole story—from start to finish, in gruesome details. We heard all about her fourteen-hour labor. Her story made me wish I never called. Words like *stitches* and *epidural* and *hemorrhoids* terrified me. And Denise cried all night.

"I wish I could just die," she wailed. "I'll never bear the pain!"

Though Tiffany repeatedly told her to shut up and go to sleep, I shared her feelings of terror. And I was pretty sure Tiffany did too.

Denise and I called Tamika's hospital room again the day she was scheduled to be released. She could barely speak through her tears. "He's so beautiful," she said. "I don't want to leave him."

Though Tamika had opted for an open adoption, agreeing with the adoptive parents that she'd receive pictures and letters until the child reached his first birthday, I could imagine the thoughts that passed through her mind. She would leave the hospital without the child she'd carried for nine months. I couldn't think of anything more difficult.

Later that morning, my social worker had arranged for a meeting with three sets of prospective adoptive parents for my child. I would have the opportunity to interview them and determine which would be the best fit for my baby—just as Tamika had done.

The first couple I interviewed were the Johanssens—a very tall man and a much shorter woman. They were Methodists. I'd insisted my child be adopted by a Christian family, so they told me all about their church and their children—they had five: three of their own and two adopted. They brought me a photo album of their family. It seemed like a picture-perfect family. They had three girls and two boys. To even out the gender split, they wanted one more boy. My boy.

"We love children," Mrs. Johanssen said. I had no doubt they did. I met two other sets of parents that day, but Mr. and Mrs. Johanssen were my favorite.

That night, I couldn't sleep. I envisioned the face of my baby, a tan-skinned boy with Steven's dark hair and my hazel eyes. I saw his picture in the Johanssen family album, a crooked smile spread across his face like grape jelly. I saw my son as a toddler, scampering amid other children who looked nothing like him. It didn't seem real.

I kept telling myself that adoption was the best thing for everyone. I wanted my child to have a good life, a mom and dad who were together, brothers and sisters who loved him. I couldn't give him any of that.

Denise couldn't sleep either. "Are you awake?" she asked.

"Yeah." I turned over to face her in the bed next to mine.

"I'm not giving her up."

"Who?"

"Cheryl. That's what I'm naming my baby." Denise's big brown eyes stared back at me. "I don't care what my parents say; I'm not giving her up."

Before that moment, I'd never thought about keeping my baby. But all that night, new thoughts entered my mind. I could see the five of us together: Mom, Dad, Michael, me, and the baby. Visions of this little person who looked like me, running through my parents' house, floated in and out of my mind as I watched Denise sleeping beside me. I wished she'd never mentioned it.

Dad called the following evening. As if he'd visited my dreams the night before, he said that he and Mom would support any decision I made about the baby.

"Your mom and I have been praying," he said, "and whatever you want to do, we're behind you. Even if you want to keep the baby. Just let us know what you want."

Great, I thought. The future of all our lives rested on my decision. I'd liked it better when the choice was up to Dad.

A new girl, Ruthie, moved in after Tamika left. The four of us were taking our daily two-mile walk around the house when Denise started complaining of abdominal pains. When we were about a hundred feet from the home, she suddenly dropped to her knees and hit the ground hard. "I can't walk," she yelled. Tears streamed down her cheeks. "It hurts," she cried, holding her belly. "I think I'm dying!"

"You have to walk," Tiffany demanded. But Denise wouldn't budge. We had no choice but to carry her. I grabbed one arm; Tiffany grabbed the other; Ruthie held her waist. Together we lifted Denise to her feet. Fighting panic, we staggered to the house, practically dragging Denise as she howled in pain.

Ms. Wyman grimaced when the three of us stumbled in and deposited Denise onto the closest chair. "What is going on?" she demanded.

We explained what happened as Denise whined.

Ms. Wyman instructed me to pack a bag for Denise—just as I'd done for Tamika. After retrieving a list of emergency contacts from a magnet on the fridge, Ms. Wyman phoned the neighbor and asked her to stay with us. She then called Denise's mother and stepfather in the Bronx. Finally, she dialed 911 and requested that an ambulance come to pick up Denise.

A few frightening minutes later, the ambulance arrived. The paramedics rushed in, placed Denise on a stretcher, and rolled her into the ambulance. Ms. Wyman climbed in the back.

I couldn't sleep that night without my friend. So I waited in the Night Room with Dutch and Thunder. A few minutes past midnight, Ms. Wyman entered through the back door, disheveled and visibly perturbed. "What are you doing down here?" she snapped when she saw me.

"I wanted to make sure Denise was okay."

"She's fine," she answered sternly. "She'll be back in the morning. False labor."

False labor? A smile crept onto my face. I felt selfishly happy that she would return. I knew we wouldn't be together forever, but I really wanted the chance to say good-bye to my friend.

But Denise did not return the next morning. Ms. Wyman informed me that the doctor had insisted on monitoring her. I figured Denise must have begged to stay in the hospital a little longer.

The next day, around five AM, Ms. Wyman crept into our bedroom and nudged my shoulder. "Get dressed," she whispered. Even in her quiet voice, she spoke with enough authority to jolt me to my feet in one leap. I dared not ask why. I just dressed and headed for the door, my sleeping roommates unaware of the commotion.

As Ms. Wyman led me to the van, I gathered the nerve to ask, "Where are we going?"

"To the hospital."

"Is Denise okay?"

"She's fine," she said, starting the engine. "She had her baby."

My heart danced with excitement. Not only would I see my friend and be able to say good-bye, I would meet her little girl—the precious baby who'd kept Denise up at night, kicking and squirming and moving all about as if she couldn't wait to dazzle the world with the same bright smile as her mother's.

The hospital was quiet. The halls were empty. I felt as if Ms. Wyman would realize how early it was and turn back out of respect for the sleeping patients. But the nurses smiled at her as she walked past them. As if she'd roamed the maternity ward at this hour dozens of times before. At that moment, I was sure she had.

When we entered Denise's room, I saw her holding her little girl. She smiled broadly when she saw me slink in behind Ms. Wyman, and my eyes widened in alarm when I saw her. Her hair stood straight up, wild and unmanaged. Her face was peppered with red pimples. Her eyes were puffy and bloodshot, her lips cracked and peeling. I wondered if I'd look that way when it was my turn.

"I'm so happy you're here," Denise whispered, her eyes filling with tears. I bent over to hug her and she giggled in my ear. "Tony was here."

I shook my head in disbelief. For some reason I'd expected a drastic change in her. A more grown-up Denise. But she was still the same silly girl who'd once asked me if men ovulated. The only thing different was that now she was a mother.

Her new daughter, so tiny and precious, was wrapped tightly in a white blanket with pink and blue stripes along the edges. I ran my finger along her soft skin and asked Denise if she was still planning to keep her.

She nodded. "My mom said it was okay as long as I get a job."

"How about Tony?"

She beamed. "He wants me to keep her." She gazed at the newborn in her arms. "I know Cheryl is his," she whispered. "She looks just like him."

Ms. Wyman slammed her hand against the wall, alarming Denise and me. "What's this nonsense about keeping the baby?" she barked. "You can't care for a child. You're just a child yourself. You'll ruin your life. And hers too."

"My mother said I could," Denise snapped.

"Your mother should have her head examined."

Denise bawled as if Ms. Wyman had just read her the last rights. I wanted to cry too.

"You'll have to toughen up," Ms. Wyman said, "if you want to be a mother."

Denise mumbled something about being a great mother. Doing it by herself. Not needing anyone.

Ms. Wyman shook her head in disgust as if she'd heard it all before. "I'll be back later to speak with your parents. I suggest you give some careful thought to this decision."

When we returned to the home later that day, I gave my own decision plenty of careful thought. I couldn't stop thinking about Denise being a teenage mother.

I thought more about it the following day and even after Denise went back to the Bronx—with Cheryl.

Whether or not to keep the baby wasn't a decision I wanted to make on my own.

17   Child In Labor

Dad and Michael visited me at the home one day when I was nearly nine months pregnant.

I awoke early that morning, though I could barely keep my eyes open from exhaustion. The previous two nights had been awful: tossing and turning, in and out of bed, at least a dozen trips to the bathroom. If I'd had any pain at all, I'd have thought it was *time*.

Dad picked me up at eleven and took me to the nearby mall for lunch. I ordered a burger, fries, and a chocolate milkshake.

I felt fine at lunch—no pain, nothing unusual. But shortly after, while riding the escalator in the mall, I felt a gush of watery discharge drench my shorts. I told Dad something was wrong, but I wasn't sure what.

"Are you in pain?" he asked.

"No." Nothing felt out of the ordinary except the surge of water that leaked into my shorts every few minutes.

Dad rushed me back to the girls' home. I changed clothes and assured him that everything was fine. The leaking had dissipated. He and Michael, convinced enough to leave me there, headed home.

"What are you doing back so soon?" Ms. Wyman asked when she saw me.

I told her about the discharge. She questioned me relentlessly. "What color was it? What was its thickness? How much? Do you feel any pain? Any pressure?"

I gave her several shoulder shrugs and ambiguous statements. Finally, she gave me a small strip of cellophane tape and told me to hold it over the discharge for a minute. "If it turns black, we need to go the hospital right away."

I marched up to the bathroom and I held the strip over the discharge. Within a few seconds, the thing was black. My eyes widened in panic. This was it. I wanted to curl into bed and pretend it wasn't happening. Maybe if I slept long enough it would all go away. I'd wake up from this crazy nightmare and realize it was all a dream. But I'd already tried that, and it didn't work. This was real, and I had to deal with it.

I threw everything I owned in the suitcase Michael and I had packed a few months prior. My heart thumped. My hands shook. I squished in the last of my clothes in a crumpled mess, zipped the suitcase, and dragged it down the long stairway.

When Ms. Wyman saw me, she shrieked, "What on earth are you doing?"

"It's time," I answered. "I'm in labor."

"I'll be the judge of that," she snapped. "If you were in any capacity to make a reliable judgment, you wouldn't be here. Now, take that case back upstairs."

"But that tape you gave me is black," I said.

"Where is it?"

"In the trash."

"Bring it to me."

I dropped my bag and scurried up the stairs. I rooted through the wastebasket for my tape. As I crouched beside the basket, I felt a pulling in my abdomen and then pressure. It was definitely time.

When I turned to leave the bathroom, I saw Ms. Wyman standing in the hall. I placed the tape in her awaiting hand. She inspected it like a scientist looking through a microscope. Then she nodded firmly and looked at me. "Your water broke. We need to get you to the hospital."

I could've told you that.

Like my predecessors, I waved good-bye to Tiffany and the new girl. It was now my turn to endure whatever came between the ambulance ride and post-delivery.

The emergency room was crowded when Ms. Wyman and I entered. People with bloody fingers. People brought in on stretchers. People sleeping on the floor and in chairs.

Ms. Wyman headed straight to the registration counter, where she gave the attending nurse my name, address, insurance information, and age. She answered all the nurse's questions in short, precise statements. I could hardly believe the young woman she spoke about was me.

Ms. Wyman told me to sit and wait. "It may take a few minutes," she said, then disappeared into a mesh of people.

While I waited, I made two collect calls: first to my mother and then to Steven.

"I'm at the hospital," I said when he answered.

"For what?"

"What do you think?"

"You're having it?"

"Not this second, but yes, I'm being admitted."

The only noise I heard was the clamor around me: shuffling feet, chattering people, intercoms, pagers.

"Did you hear me?"

"Yeah."

"Well?"

"I don't know if I can get up there tonight."

I slammed down the receiver and stared at the pay phone, my eyes filling with tears. Somewhere in the back of my mind, I clung to a glimmer of hope, a dream perhaps, that somehow things could be normal. That even at this late stage, I could assemble a family: mother, father, and baby. But no. Nothing had changed. I stood there, searching my mind for answers, accepting rejection once more, gathering the strength to carry the burden alone. *This was never God's will for me.*

"Stephanie!" Ms. Wyman called. Her voice resonated through the crowd of listless people. "Your chair is ready."

I turned and saw Ms. Wyman standing beside an empty wheelchair. It waited like a throne for a goddess. For me.

A hospital technician took the chair and wheeled it toward me, zigzagging around tables and people. He nodded and smiled, reaching out to grab my hand. "Your ride, madame." Without hesitation, I took his hand and planted myself in the chair. He scooted me through the crowd to my hospital room, leaving Ms. Wyman behind.

My room was almost a replica of Denise's, but smaller. Same smells, same pink floral wallpaper covering the lower half of the walls, same wooden chair rail. The room was directly across from the nurses' station. If I craned my neck, I could see the tops of their heads behind the desk. It was comforting to know they were there.

Once I put on the drab hospital gown that would comprise my entire wardrobe for the next few days, a nurse came in and hooked my belly up to a machine that monitored my contractions. She stuck a needle into my right arm and started an IV. She asked if I felt okay. I shrugged. I'd forgotten what okay felt like.

"You'll be fine," she assured me.

I hoped she was right.

Ms. Wyman wobbled in a half hour after I entered my room. "Well, how are you?" she asked brashly, plopping into a cushioned seat beside me, releasing a heavy sigh.

"Okay," I answered, not really knowing if it were true.

She leaned close to the monitor and asked if I was in pain.

"Not really."

"You're having contractions," she said. "They're about midlevel."

"What's that mean?"

"Means they'll get worse."

"How much worse?"

She shrugged. "Denise was crying like a baby when she was at this level. But you didn't even realize you were having contractions."

The nurse came in and checked to see if I had dilated. Only three centimeters. That meant I'd have to wait. The nurse told me I'd probably have the baby sometime in the morning. "Get some rest," she recommended.

Dad came in several hours later with Aunt Jo Ann, Uncle Robert's wife. Since Mom didn't want to be there for the birth of the grandson she would never know, she asked Aunt Jo Ann to be there with me. Like Uncle Robert, Aunt Jo Ann was a strong Christian.

After kissing my cheek as soon as she entered the room, she led Dad and me in prayer. She asked for specific things: that the Lord would be with me during the delivery, that He would give me peace, that He would make it a painless and speedy delivery, a natural process that would require no drugs. An instant calm swept through me when she said amen. Almost as if her prayers were already answered.

Sitting beside me at the edge of the hospital bed, holding my hand, she asked sweetly, "How are you, honey? Can I get you anything?"

"Water, please, with ice," I answered.

She smiled, and quickly rushed out to the nurse and asked for water. My dad lingered by the door, staring at me. My belly bulged beneath a stiff blanket, monitors beeping and blinking all around me. His eyes looked clouded with questions—how had I lost my way, what could he have done or not done to keep me from such an ordeal? I knew this was by far the hardest thing he'd ever had to do.

I Took the Long Way Home

My aunt swished back in, holding a cup of ice chips, and sat in a chair beside my bed. I saw Dad leave just as Aunt Jo Ann lifted the first ice chip into my mouth. It soothed my dry mouth, while the rest of me ached in discomfort. I knew there was nothing left to do but wait.

Around two AM Steven strolled into the hospital room with his friend Mikey. They both looked like they'd come from the campus bar. Their hair was damp and unkempt; their clothes reeked of beer. Aunt Jo Ann cringed at the sight of them. So did I.

His nonchalant attitude convinced me that Mom and Dad were right about everything. About Steven. About love. About relationships. I wished I listened to them and waited.

Just as Aunt Jo Ann had prayed for, my delivery was quick and virtually painless. It didn't even last an hour. The doctor walked into the delivery room, told me to push, and out the baby came. No drugs required. Totally natural.

I learned much later that Aunt Jo Ann wasn't the only one praying. Mom and Dad's whole church cried out to God on my behalf. Some gathered together in prayer for me from the time Mom informed them I'd gone into labor to the moment she called to tell them I had delivered.

At 3:44 AM I gave birth to my baby boy. Domenic Antonio Cavelli. The nurses placed him on my chest for a moment before they carried him off to weigh and measure him. His cry was faint and fragile—it sounded like a cat meowing.

"Will I get to see him again?" I asked as I lay there, helpless, watching the nurses handle him expertly. They assured me I would, later, as they whisked us both away to our separate domains—me to the recovery room and him to the nursery. It all happened so fast.

I wondered if I really would get to see my child. Or if Ms. Wyman had conspired with the doctors and nurses to keep me from seeing him. Perhaps that was the reason for her unusual kindness. All sorts of thoughts raced through my mind as the nurses wheeled me into the dark recovery room. If I'd had any strength, I would have voiced my concerns. But the second I entered the room I nodded off to sleep.

After several hours, I awoke and the nurses wheeled me back to my hospital room. There, in a mobile crib, lay a tiny boy, wrapped snugly in a white blanket. My whole body warmed at the sight of him. His face was pink and shriveled like a raisin, and he was even more beautiful than I envisioned. I'd never seen anything so perfect.

"Can I hold him?" I asked the nurse who stood over his crib.

"Please do," she said.

He looked so peaceful and delicate; I almost didn't want to trouble him.

As I reached to scoop up my son for the first time, I heard Ms. Wyman's voice in my mind, the instructions she'd given each of us girls concerning post-delivery. "Don't even hold the babies," she told us. "Just makes it harder to say good-bye." I'd always wondered how she knew. I could only surmise that she'd seen enough tearful farewells in her lifetime. Maybe mine wouldn't end so sorrowfully.

As I held and examined my son, I saw a little Cavelli in him. He had our nose, our mouth. In every way, he was ours. I wanted desperately to keep him. But I wasn't sure. I wanted to love him. But I wished he'd come a little later in my life.

My social worker visited later that day, but she had no answers for me. Neither did Dad or Mom. It was my decision. The destiny of this little person's life was in my hands. But I didn't know what to do. I wished I could disappear to some faraway place where I never had to decide anything.

A'nanni visited with flowers and chocolates, but I didn't want either. I yelled at her for bringing gifts. I told her there was nothing to celebrate. She apologized and cried.

"Why are you crying?" I asked her. "I'm the one in pain. I'm in the hospital. What have you got to cry about? You don't have any life-altering decisions to make." She was still a virgin. She'd followed the rules. I was the only one allowed to cry.

"I'm sorry," she repeated over and over. Finally I asked her to leave. The one person who'd been with me through everything, my best friend since fourth grade, and I couldn't stand the sight of her. She was everything I wished I could be. She was free.

After two days in the hospital, I still hadn't made up my mind. Each day, I held my son Domenic, kissing him and loving him as if I'd see him for the rest of my life. I used six rolls of film taking pictures of him, his hands and feet and mouth and ears. Just in case I never saw him again—in case I forgot how perfect

I TOOK THE LONG WAY HOME

and precious he was. I didn't know how it would all end, but I wanted to prepare for both possibilities. Each scenario had distinct elements of fear. Fear of raising a child and fear of losing one. I had to decide which I could live with.

My social worker informed me that I could take up to two weeks to make a decision. The child would stay in foster care until I made up my mind. After those two weeks, I would have to decide. She advised me to go home, get readjusted with life, and then make a decision. I'd have sounder judgment that way. Dad and Mom encouraged me to do just that.

On the day of my release from the hospital, another social worker came to pick up Domenic just as Dad and I were leaving. She gave me a few moments to say good-bye. As if anyone could say good-bye to her child in just a few moments.

Dad held Domenic in his arms and cried hard and loud. "This is my grandson," he moaned. "My grandson." After kissing his nose and cheeks and head, tears falling onto Domenic's sleeping face, Dad handed him back to me and left the room.

I cradled my baby in my arms. His face was tranquil, his eyes gently shut, his tiny lips moving in and out as if he were sucking a bottle. I wished I could leave him just as he was—an infant— and come back to get him when I was older and married and finished with adolescence. I wanted freedom, but I wanted my baby. I wanted a career and a husband and a house of my own, but I wanted Domenic too.

There was only one problem: the career and husband and home could wait; Domenic couldn't.

18

And then Came Baby

I went home from the hospital that day without Domenic.

It didn't take long for me to readjust. It seemed as if my old life had been held in the lost and found, just waiting for me to claim it. Friends, family, work, school—all still there. But one uncertainty lingered: Would Domenic join our family?

It was a question I couldn't answer.

Every morning for six days, Mom and Dad asked, "Have you decided?" And every morning, I gave the same answer: "Not yet." But I knew I couldn't keep avoiding the decision. Very soon I needed to decide whether to sign my son's life over to adoptive parents or raise him myself.

There were so many considerations. I didn't know if I wanted to sacrifice my freedom and normalcy, my dreams. And of course there was Domenic, this defenseless person whose destiny depended on my decision. It didn't seem fair.

Dad and Mom requested prayer from our church family for wisdom and discernment. What had seemed so clear just a few months earlier was now clouded with indecision.

We had lots of visitors at the house—mostly people from church. Some came with simple words of encouragement while others specifically urged us to keep Domenic.

"What better home than yours to raise a child in?"

"Domenic is your special gift."

"God has a plan for his life."

Seemed like everyone knew for sure but me.

Early on the morning of the seventh day after my release from the hospital, Mom and Dad entered my room and woke me. With my eyes half open, I saw their faces hovering above me. They looked more excited than I'd seen them in months.

"Well?" Mom asked as my blurry eyes tried to adjust. "Have you decided what to do?"

I shook my head, still groggy.

"Well, we've decided for you." She nudged my dad with her elbow, restraining a smile. "We want you to keep him." Smiles spread across their faces.

I woke instantly, sitting straight up, my eyes wide and alert. "What?"

"We think you should keep him," Dad confirmed. "We'll raise him as a family."

"Get dressed," Mom said giddily. "We're going shopping."

That morning, I withdrew all the money in my savings account and purchased what I needed to care for my new son: car seat, diapers, bathtub, monitor, and formula.

By noon, Mom had called both families (blood relatives and the church) to share the news. By dinnertime, we'd had at least fifty visitors and received enough baby supplies and clothes to last for two years.

That night, as I prepared for bed, Mom poked her head in my room and told me to enjoy my last night of uninterrupted sleep. "It'll be the last the last in a long time," she said. In just one day, I'd exchanged my young life for motherhood. Never could I have anticipated the radical change from one day to the next

The following morning Dad and I picked up Domenic from the foster family. I sat beside him in the backseat on the ride home. He was so small that even in the infant car seat we had to pad the sides of his head and body with blankets. He slept most of the way and I watched his innocent face, oblivious to the circumstances surrounding his arrival into the world. I wondered if one day I'd be able to share my experience with him.

Mom was waiting anxiously at the door when we arrived with her new grandson. Her eyes lit up when she saw him. She scooped him from my arms before I could make it through the door and whisked him into the kitchen and living room and all over the house, talking in a baby language all her own. "This is your new house, my little angel," she whispered, "and we'll take very good care of you."

Domenic wasn't at his new home long before Dad asked if I had told Steven.

I hadn't.

"You need to tell him right away," Dad insisted.

Steven and his family were aware that Domenic was in foster care while I made my decision, and they'd all been surprisingly supportive. "It's your decision," Steven reiterated as he'd done the night of our meeting. "If you want to keep him, you know I'll be here for you."

Just as he promised, within an hour of telling him, Steven and his family came to the house with gifts and video cameras, assuring us they'd be involved in Domenic's life.

Even Mrs. Donato was behaved, congratulating my parents and speaking as if Domenic's birth had instantly merged us into one big family. "You're like a daughter to me now," she told me. "I want you to call me whenever you need anything."

But my mom was convinced that beneath her kindness skulked an ulterior motive. "I don't trust her for a second."

She was right. Three months later, when Mrs. Donato didn't see Domenic as often as she thought she should, she coerced Steven into taking me to court for joint custody.

Suddenly everyone wanted the child that no one had wanted.

Having never been summoned to a courtroom, my parents and I panicked when the certified court order arrived in the mail. We agonized over what would happen, thinking the judge would make us hand over Domenic to be raised by Steven and his family. "Lord, how could You give us this gift and then take him away?" we cried. All we could do was trust Him.

Mom, Dad, and I assembled in the county courthouse with Steven and his mother the day of the hearing.

But fortunately, our turn in family court was only minimally painful. The judge ordered that Domenic visit with Steven every other weekend and every other holiday. "And the father must be present," the judge added.

"My son has a full academic scholarship to Penn State," Mrs. Donato informed the judge proudly. "He can't always make it home on weekends."

"Your son's first priority is being a father," the judge barked. "He'd better make it his business to be home to see his son. Otherwise, I don't know why you're wasting my time."

Mrs. Donato's eyebrows rose.

Steven assured the judge that he'd be home on those weekends even if he had to walk. "I love my son."

"Good," the judge said. "You'll need to get a job, too, because you'll have to pay for child support."

"Child support?" Mrs. Donato exclaimed. "But my son is a student. He needs to study. He doesn't have time for a job."

"Your boy is also a father, and he needs to support his child. Love doesn't buy diapers."

My parents and I sat there, astonished at how plainly the judge spoke to Steven and his mother.

I TOOK THE LONG WAY HOME

I sat there in shock, waiting for our turn. Surely the judge would turn to me and say, "And as for you, young lady…"

Instead, after only ten minutes in the courtroom, we were politely dismissed.

Though Steven's college campus was only four hours away, his promised every-other-weekend visits quickly turned into just one weekend a month. "I have a ton of work to do," he'd tell me. "There's no way I can make it down this weekend." Meanwhile, in the background, I'd hear the voices of screaming girls and the obnoxious laughter of guys.

He called daily but I rarely spoke with him. I let Dad answer his calls. He would kindly tell Steven how Domenic was doing.

"He had a great day."

"Rolled over for the first time."

"Got his first tooth."

At times, I wanted to pick up the extension and say, "Give it up, Dad. Do you really think he cares?"

Maybe I was just jealous. Part of me wished I was as free as Steven.

But life was different for me. My last two years of high school—the years when normal kids attended proms, flew to Florida for spring break, and prepared for SATs—were filled with changing diapers and daycare drop-off and pick-up. While kids in the youth group attended another missions trip, I warmed bottles, watched Sesame Street, and spent many sleepless nights. I saw pictures and videos of my friends at their proms, heard stories about senior week in Palm Beach, Florida. I sat in church and listened to the youth group share their experiences on the mission field, testifying of God's miracles. I wondered if I would ever testify of such miracles.

At the end of my senior year in high school, I attended A'nanni's graduation ceremony and watched enviously as she was honored for academic achievement. President of her school council and an active participant in various extracurricular activities, she beamed with pride as she strode down the aisle to accept her diploma. I tried to be happy for her, but couldn't shake the feeling of shame when I compared her life with mine.

I'd struggled to graduate. To help with daycare and other expenses, I worked twenty hours a week. By the time I came home each night from work, I was exhausted. I didn't have the focus or the strength for homework. Bath and story time had replaced studying. And Domenic still woke up in the night, making it difficult for me to remain alert during my classes.

I longed for the freedom I once knew, the carefree spirit I'd relinquished for motherhood. But that life was a memory, part of a distant past that seemed unrecoverable.

Even when I wanted to go to the mall with friends after work, Dad would say, "No. You have a child to feed and bathe. You need to be home."

"I just want to go for an hour," I argued.

"Stephanie," Dad said calmly, "every choice we make in life has a consequence. You're a mother now. You can't come and go as you used to."

Despite Mom and Dad's daily reminders, and my slow adjustment to accepting my new role, I could never have managed without their help. Mom called Domenic "the family baby." And he certainly was. We all had a hand in his rearing. Even Michael.

The church family embraced him too. When he was a baby, he was passed from woman to woman during services like an offering plate, each wanting her turn at holding the pastor's grandson. When he learned how to walk, he darted from pew to pew, hugging the women, accepting their gifts of candy and mints.

Mom loved to have him sit in the sanctuary with her during song service. Most mothers couldn't wait to drop their kids in the church nursery, but my mom insisted that Domenic be present for worship. "He loves the songs," she said when I teasingly questioned her motives. "Just look at the way he enjoys the music." I watched him roll along the carpet and slide across the pew and realize my mother really just wanted to show off her grandbaby.

Sometimes, during quiet moments between songs, Domenic would climb onto the pew and wave at my father on the platform. "Hi, Poppie!" he'd shout.

Dad smiled while the congregation chuckled. "At least someone's enjoying the service," he'd joke.

My parents spoke of Domenic as if he was their own, as if there was something missing in our lives before he came along. They simply adored him.

When the opportunity came for me to attend college, my parents offered to take care of Domenic for me temporarily. "We want you to have the same opportunities as Steven," Mom

I TOOK THE LONG WAY HOME

told me. "The best thing you can do for your son is to get an education."

It didn't take any convincing on my end. I packed my bags gladly and followed A'nanni to West Chester University, where we both enrolled as liberal arts majors.

College was an hour's drive from my house, so I was close enough to visit Domenic on weekends but far enough away to reclaim the life I once knew.

I settled into my role as a full-time student with ease. College felt safe, and being a full-time university student was something I quickly mastered. I earned straight-As. Unlike many other freshmen, I had a mission: to earn a degree so I could eventually support my son.

I also decided to serve the Lord. I joined Campus Crusade for Christ and befriended other believers. I woke early each morning for prayer with a group of Christians in my dorm. And for the first time in a long time, I felt at peace. No lying, no sneaking around, no hiding. I worked, studied, prayed, and read the Bible. After so much turmoil and stress, my freshman year was a time of rest.

Things changed during sophomore year, however. The excitement of college living, among thousands of unsaved students, gradually enticed me. My eyes, which had been so focused on Christ, shifted. My commitment to Jesus was replaced by distractions such as overachievement, a boyfriend, friends, and parties. Though most were acceptable distractions, they led to a preoccupation with the world and the illusions that surround it, and ultimately led me astray.

Sometime during his senior year, Steven became very serious about his life. He finally cleaned up his act. He quit drinking and smoking, and he came home every other weekend to see Domenic. Determined to graduate with honors and get accepted to a prestigious law school, he moved into a one bedroom apartment and spent much of his time studying. "I want Domenic to be proud of me," he told me.

As Steven neared completion of undergraduate school, he also wanted to settle down. He requested a private meeting and when I asked why, he said he had a proposition to discuss with me.

We met at a diner one weekend when we were both home. "I think we should get married," he announced over BLT sandwiches. "For Domenic's sake."

"Are you serious?" I asked, nearly choking.

"Yes," he confirmed as if the marriage were some kind of business deal. "I'm moving back to Philly and I think we should be together. A family. It's best for Domenic."

Blindsided by his offer, I told him I had to think about it.

At twenty, I couldn't imagine myself married—especially to Steven. I no longer had any feelings for him. I didn't love him or hate him. He was just Domenic's father. He also wasn't a believer.

"Steven thinks we should get married for Domenic's sake," I told my father when I returned home from dinner.

My father waved a finger at me. "You already made one mistake," he said, his voice raised. "You're not making another one."

He didn't even have to pray about it.

But I knew Steven was not someone I could spend my life with. Though he was Domenic's father, he could never be my husband. Convenience was not a criterion for marriage.

I e-mailed him my answer: *It wouldn't work.*

We never spoke of it again.

Instead, Steven and I concentrated on our careers and our separate lives. He graduated law school the same year I graduated from college.

My exit from college was nothing like my exit from high school. This time, A'nanni and I walked down the aisle together, each of us recognized for honors and accomplishments we had achieved. My parents were pleased. Domenic was proud. It made me happy to honor them.

Steven became engaged to a girl named Cara during his last year of law school. She was a fellow student and a beautiful girl. But she never smiled. When I asked Steven about her, he told me her family was wealthy. I couldn't understand how her family's wealth made her a good life partner.

Steven must have agreed, because the day after they called off the engagement, he booked a vacation to Maui with three of his high school buddies. He told me they were celebrating his "prison release."

A year later, Steven told me he'd fallen in love with Charlotte Tucker, a blonde actress from Tennessee. They'd met while she was in Philadelphia, acting in an independent feature film on which Steven had secured the permits for various locations throughout the city. Steven had passed the bar exam and was ready for the next item on his life agenda. They married within six months.

Though I couldn't understand their rush, I thought Charlotte was good for Steven, and good for Domenic too. She was sweet and genuine and wanted to raise lots of babies. I just wasn't sure if Steven shared that desire.

They had a daughter, Savannah, shortly before their first anniversary. Domenic loved her. "I wish my baby sister could live with us," he told me.

They seemed like the perfect couple, and their relationship worked—for a while. They divorced after three years of marriage.

My love life wasn't as newsworthy. I had a boyfriend the last two years of college, but I knew it wouldn't last. He wanted a conventional life: nine-to-five job, a couple of kids. But I felt so strongly that there was more out there, a greater love I hadn't yet found.

Having not found that love in men or in friends, I resolved to find it elsewhere. *Surely*, I thought, *I would find it on my own eventually.*

Instead of seeking the Lord, the One in whom I'd once found peace and rest, I sought for love in career success. Certainly wealth would fulfill my longing.

After graduating from college, I secured a stable job with plenty of room for advancement. At the age of twenty–one, I purchased my first home. I moved Domenic out of Mom and Dad's house and began raising him as a single mother.

But when working forty hours a week and raising a son alone turned out to be less than glamorous, I decided I wanted to go to Hollywood and become a screenwriter. Certainly notoriety would satisfy.

I told my family I was going to quit my secure, great-paying job and move to Los Angeles. "My life is on the West Coast," I proclaimed.

When I informed Steven of my plans, he threatened to have me in court the same afternoon to petition for physical custody of Domenic. At that point I realized Hollywood would have to wait.

So I determined to climb corporate ladders in hopes of earning the status and wealth I desired. I gave up dating, and concentrated on my career and raising Domenic.

But all the while, as I depended on myself and leaned on my own understanding, going from one project to the next, one goal to the next, I felt an intense pursuit on my life. Not by men, but by a Redeemer who wanted the life I'd once given him. He never gave up on me. Relentless, He knocked on the door of my heart, waiting to be let in. Subtle. Persistent.

But I ignored His calling, trusting rather in the life I had designed for myself. I sought fulfillment in things, forfeiting the approval of God to gain the applause of man.

And that love I longed for continued to elude me—year after year as I took the long way home.

Then I met Gregory.

I'd written a screenplay that a well-known producer was interested in optioning, and I needed a lawyer to review the contract before I signed it. Steven recommended someone he knew that specialized in entertainment law. He gave me a card that read Gregory R. London, Esq., Attorney at Law. "Call him," Steven advised. "He's a great guy. You'll love him."

I e-mailed Gregory the following day and arranged to meet him at his office. Our meeting was scheduled for nine AM, but I arrived a half hour early, with hopes of getting things done before I was due in to work.

I sat in the reception area, anxiously tapping my fingernails on an end table, watching as several suited men zipped past me with briefcases and file folders. I expected that one of them would eventually introduce himself as Gregory. None did.

At a quarter till nine, a tall, burly guy traipsed through the lobby doors in sweatpants, carrying a gym bag in one hand and a briefcase in the other. His hair was wet, as if he'd just showered. His face was freshly shaven and his clothes were wrinkled. He stopped at the receptionist's desk and asked if he had any messages.

"Yes." The woman pointed in my direction. "The young lady over there is waiting for you."

He whipped his head around and looked at me in horror. I waved. If he wasn't so adorable looking, I'd have been annoyed.

I Took the Long Way Home

He walked over and apologized. The scent of soap pervaded the air around him. "I am so sorry for your wait. I wasn't expecting you so early. I just came from the gym. Give me a minute to dress."

Gaining my approval, he scooted away then returned within minutes wearing a pinstriped suit, his hair combed, and smelling like cologne. He escorted me to his office, where we talked and laughed and completed the paperwork.

As the meeting ended Gregory asked if I'd consider going out with him. "Now that you've seen me in sweats and sneakers, I guess I can't lose."

"You won't be wearing those on the date, will you?" I teased.

He promised he'd save them for the gym.

But even while I dated Gregory, I still felt I hadn't found that love I longed for. There was still something missing, a barrenness that no earthly romance could quench.

It wasn't until my New Year's encounter—the night I re-met Jesus—that I finally found the Love my heart so desperately desired. That New Year's revelation triggered a transformation in my life, my heart, and my motives that would forever change me.

19   An Old Friend

In the first year after my life-altering revelation, I totally and completely fell in love with Jesus Christ and His eternal Word—more so than I ever did as a child. There was no turning back for me. My heart had finally found its home.

But this revelation, this commitment—my new understanding of Christ's sacrifice for me—was no guarantee of a perfect life. I learned through the Word that God never promised life without heartache and trouble. And temptation. But He did promise that He would never leave me nor forsake me.[xlvi] As a new Christian, I clung to those words: *never leave, never forsake*. When I experienced alienation from friends or the aloneness of not having a steady boyfriend, or when temptation taunted me, that promise kept me going.

For a time I experienced a bitter sadness in response to my separation from Gregory. But the Lord faithfully carried me through that time. He showed me that I could depend on Him and find solace and comfort in Him. He proved that He could fulfill all my needs, spiritually and emotionally. He could truly be that friend, that partner, that refuge for which my soul yearned.

My friends didn't know what to think of the new Stephanie. They accepted my decision but didn't understand my salvation—or the change they saw in me. They didn't know that in all the years I had lived in separation from my heavenly Father I never felt at home. I always felt like a stranger in the world, an alien. I never belonged there. It was always a forced fit. I pretended as if I belonged—so much so that no one would have guessed my dissatisfaction. I finally understood what Mom meant all those years. As Christians, we *are* aliens and strangers in this world.[xlvii]

My friends simply concluded the same thing as Gregory: that my parents had finally gotten to me.

A week before Christmas, almost a year after my revelation, I was working late one night. The office was deserted except for me, the CEO, and the receptionist, Desiree, a pleasant African-American woman in her early twenties.

I'd promised my biggest client that I'd provide pricing for a program he wanted initiated in January, and I was determined to finish it before leaving. I asked Desiree to hold all calls except for emergencies from friends or family and she knew my short list of friends and family members who'd justify such an interruption.

My office door locked, cell phone turned off, and the quiet of an empty office settling around me, I felt confident I would finish within the hour. My fingers whizzed across the keyboard, stroking letters and numbers and symbols with precision.

Midway through the proposal, Desiree's voice crackled through my phone. "Excuse me, Steph, I have your friend Kelly on the line. She says it's an emergency."

Kelly was the last person who'd make such a claim unless warranted. "I'll take it." I lifted the phone to my ear. "This is Stephanie."

"Damian is dead," Kelly said. "He shot himself last night."

Damian who? I thought. I held my breath, trying to piece together arbitrary memories of a mutual acquaintance. Could Damian be someone from college? An uncle of hers? A partner at Gregory's firm? I couldn't place him.

"Can you believe it?" she asked. "The guy shoots himself a week before Christmas. I mean, he looked so happy last year on New Year's."

Wait. Last year's New Year's Eve party. Penthouse condo on the water. The rich entertainment lawyer. Okay, got it.

"The guy had everything," she added. "I can't imagine what would make him do it. It's bizarre."

"Yeah," I muttered.

"Did you already know?"

"No, this is the first I'm hearing of it."

"You don't sound surprised. I thought maybe Gregory told you or something."

"I haven't talked to Gregory in months."

"Well, everyone's saying he was on drugs. I heard he's been pretty out of it lately. I talked to his girlfriend last night, and she said he'd been talking crazy for the last few weeks. She's the one who found him—facedown in a puddle of blood on the kitchen table."

Images of Damian from a year ago moved through my mind like a movie reel: his eloquent speech, movie star looks, the empty sadness I noticed. *This man—the picture of success—is now eternally separated from his Creator.* He had everything money could buy, everything to satisfy his physical desires, but nothing to satisfy his soul. Damian died without ever having lived.

"The viewing's Wednesday. We should all go."

"I can't," I answered without even considering it.

"Listen, Steph, I know you found God or whatever. And that's cool if it works for you. But you act like you can't be around us anymore. Like you're too good for us or something."

"It's not that—"

"We've barely seen you in the past year," she scolded. "You don't even return our phone calls."

"My life is just different now," I told her. "I'm different."

"I know, I know. You told me all about the 'new creature' thing. But you can be different and still be our friend, can't you?"

"I'm sorry." I paused, holding the phone with my shoulder and typing the last few words of a sentence. "I'll try to be more diligent about seeing you guys."

"So you'll come to the viewing?"

"I don't think so," I answered, pressing spell check on the menu bar of my computer.

"What kind of Christian are you that you can't even come to your friend's viewing?"

"He was really more Gregory's friend than mine."

"So what? You knew him too."

"Yeah, by face, but—"

"But what?"

"I barely knew the guy," I mumbled, switching the phone to my other shoulder.

"You know all his friends. You were practically married to one of them. You're part of the circle. You have to go. Everybody's gonna be there."

A year ago, I'd have jumped at the opportunity to be where "everyone" was. But now, having found the true purpose of life, I didn't need to be where everyone else was.

"What if Gregory's there with his new wife?" I said.

"Even better," she teased. "We can throw things at them."

A laugh escaped. Kelly was always great at making light of any situation. "It's on Wednesday?"

"Yeah. Should only take a few hours in the morning. It's a closed-casket viewing, and then the funeral."

"I guess I can go."

"Good," she said, sounding pleased. "It'll be nice to see you again. I hear a lot of his friends are in shambles. The family, too. Maybe you can say a few prayers on their behalf."

"I will," I promised. "I certainly will."

It teemed all Wednesday morning. The downpour drenched the streets so badly I nearly canceled.

Awaiting a cab, I stood beneath my awning and inhaled the cold December air. Raindrops pelted car windows and assembled in deep puddles along the sidewalks. I stood amazed at the thought of a God who loved us enough to send rain to water the earth.[xlviii] A smile escaped at the wonder of a God who cared for me.

The rain slowed a bit just as a yellow cab pulled up in front of me. I dashed inside.

I arrived at St. Peter's Cathedral close to nine AM. Before exiting the cab I whispered a quick prayer. *Lord, let my light shine. Your Word says I'm the light of the world.*[xlix] *Let them see it in me.*

Despite the rain, people were lined up for an entire block outside the church. Like a meeting of the city's elite, suited men with matching ties and handkerchiefs, and women in four-inch heels, big red lips, and diamonds all gathered with umbrellas.

I made my way into the church, foregoing the viewing and squeezing through the line for a seat in the cathedral. I looked at all the people gathered to pay their respects to Damian Alfonso Caruso. Not a single one could save him. None could give him the answer to life's most perplexing question: *What on earth am I doing here?*

I casually looked for Gregory, praying for strength that I could bear seeing him. *He'll be late if he shows up at all,* I thought as I entered the foyer outside the sanctuary.

My friends were huddled in a corner like teenagers at a school dance: Janette, Kelly and Sicily. I joined them and they greeted me with hugs. They asked how I was doing, how Domenic was doing in school, and when we could all get together under different circumstances. It was good to see them.

Sicily, a big-boned, fast-talking girl with short dark hair spoke about a man in line who'd recently purchased a multi-million-dollar beachfront property in Ocean City, New Jersey, and a couple who, prior to marrying, each owned a top advertising company in the city. They had merged forces and now ran the leading agency in the area. "I brought two hundred business cards," she said. "I could probably make more contacts here than at any networking party."

I shot a disgusted glance at Kelly, who looked equally annoyed. "We're here to support the family," she reprimanded.

"I'm kidding," Sicily said.

I rolled my eyes. *Help me, Jesus*

"Should we get in line to greet the family?" Janette asked.

"The service is supposed to start in twenty minutes," I said. "I think we should just find seats."

As we moved into the sanctuary, I took note of the exit—just in case I needed to slip out for a quick escape.

Inside the large Catholic cathedral, adorned with statues of St. Peter and a large crucifix affixed to the front wall, I found a crowd of people already seated, including some familiar faces. I greeted Michelle, the girl who did my makeup for several formal dinners I attended with Gregory, a limo driver Gregory and I used for several trips to and from New York, and a guy I knew from my gym. While hugging each with a sigh of regret, I felt someone's eyes on me, searching my face, my motions, my words. It was unmistakably an ex-boyfriend's glare. Gregory was in the building. Though I was tempted to scan the pews for him and his new missus, I chose to sit and be still. And Pray.

Kelly sat beside me and began speaking to one of Damian's cousins, a woman in her mid-fifties who couldn't have been more than five feet tall. Kelly expressed her sorrow for the family's loss.

"He was a wonderful person," she gushed. "None of us can imagine why he'd do such a thing."

I considered the fragility of life. God's Word tells us that we are but a vapor, a whisper.[li] We're here on this earth for a little while and then gone. I wondered if anyone else in the room had contemplated his or her eternal destiny. Nothing like the funeral of a man whose life ended prematurely to evoke such questions.

I felt someone pat my shoulder. Expecting to see a remotely familiar face, I was surprised to see Gregory. He looked at me tenderly, his lips curled up in a smile.

"Hey," he whispered, kneeling beside me in the aisle and leaning across me to kiss my cheek. His lips were soft and warm, just as I remembered them. Clad in a black suit, gray shirt, and turquoise tie, his hair combed straight back with hints of gel streaked through the front layers, he looked as handsome as ever. My eyes watered at the sight of him. As if all the hurtful memories, even those final words that cut through me like a knife, were somehow cleansed from remembrance.

"How are you?" He grabbed my hand.

"Doing well." I instinctively stroked my fingers across the back of his.

"And Domenic?"

"He's great."

After a few seconds of touching and smiling, he tugged my arm and motioned me to slip out of the room. "Come on." He nodded toward the exit. "Let's talk for a minute."

I turned to Kelly as I slid out of the pew and told her I'd be right back.

He led me down the center aisle, into the foyer, then down a corridor.

At the end of the corridor he whisked me into an empty hallway and pulled me close for a hug. "I can't believe how much I've missed you," he said in my ear, his voice low.

I held on to his broad shoulders and inhaled his intoxicating cologne, remembering all the reasons I loved him. But in the next instant, I remembered all the reasons we were no longer together. Including his wife.

My arms collapsed to my side. "Where's Melanie?"

He shrugged, visibly uncomfortable. "We broke up."

"I thought you were getting married."

"Yeah, I thought so, too, but you know…"

"No, I don't know. What?"

"Just wasn't right."

I wanted to pry but didn't. I wanted to gloat over his latest failed attempt at being happy, but I couldn't. It wasn't the Lord's way. I just assumed Melanie was an ordinary girl with flaws and quirks. Not even Gregory, with all his self-proclaimed perfections, could find Miss Perfect.

"That's too bad," I said, sincerely sorry that things hadn't worked out for him.

"Don't you want to know what happened?"

I shook my head and smiled. "It's none of my business."

His lips tightened, his eyes narrowed. "I bet you're dying to know."

"No," I said calmly. "That's between you and Melanie."

He raised his eyebrows as if to say *whatever,* and then moved on to the next subject. "So, what about you? Who're you seeing now?"

"No one."

"Sure," he said, elongating the word.

"I'm not," I said. "I'm waiting for the Lord to send me my husband."

"Oh, right, right. You're practicing your new religion."

"I'm not *practicing* anything," I corrected him. "I'm living. For Christ."

"Well, whatever you're doing, it's working." He pushed my hair behind my shoulder. "You look terrific. You're glowing."

"It's the Lord, Gregory. He's changed me."

Cupping my cheek with his hand, he looked at me with curious eyes. "I can tell. You have that look."

"What look?"

"The one your parents have. I watched you this morning from across the room. Your whole countenance has changed. I thought, *She's either in love or really committed to the whole church thing.*"

"I am in love," I said, leaning my cheek into his palm. "With Jesus."

He smiled, a genuine smile void of his usual arrogance. "I prayed the other day. When I heard about Damian." His fingers moved across my face before he dropped his hand to his waist. "We're a lot alike. We were anyway." He shook his head. "Sometimes I wonder why I'm here. I mean, is this all there is to life?" He crossed his arms. "I couldn't sleep the past few nights thinking about it. I mean, the guy shot himself. Was his life that bad?" His eyes narrowed as he placed both hands in his pockets.

His eyes roamed the floor. I marveled at how a man with so much intelligence and charm, someone with so many achievements and success, could look so lost. A man who claimed to know everything and everyone didn't know the one Person who could grant him eternal life.

"I want what you have." He looked up at me. "Whatever it costs. Whatever I have to do to get it—I want it."

I smiled and took his hand from his pocket. "It's free," I said. "A gift. All you have to do is ask for it."

20   Answered Prayer

It's Christmas day. Domenic and I are going to Mom and Dad's for what is sure to be a dinner fit for a king. Knowing Mom, she's probably been cooking for days, authentic Italian hors d'oeuvres, several entrées, including a variety of meats and pastas, and her signature chocolate mousse cake. The leftovers will undoubtedly last until the New Year.

Mom invited Uncle Robert, Aunt Jo Ann, and their three kids over, and asked us all to be there by one o'clock. Domenic and I are already running late, with just fifteen minutes to travel forty miles. Domenic is pacing outside the bathroom as I lean over the sink to squirt perfume on my wrists and neck and then apply a thin layer of lipstick. "Come on, Mom," he says, "we're gonna be late."

"We're already late," I correct him then pucker my lips to evenly spread the color. I pause for a moment as I observe my reflection. There's something very different about the woman in the mirror. Very simply—her eyes are smiling. She is at peace. The emptiness that I noticed so plainly a year ago has vanished and is now filled with a blessed assurance that Jesus is mine. A sensation of thanks permeates me. I have indeed found my way home. "Thank you Lord," I whisper.

"Let's go, Mom."

"I'm coming." I shove my makeup bag into a clutch, and scurry out of the bathroom. "Now, where are my keys?"

"I have them," he says, obviously annoyed.

"What about the desserts?" Last night I picked up two cakes from an award-winning local bakery—Dad's favorites: chocolate chip cheesecake and vanilla cannoli.

"Already in the car."

"You're the best." I grab a sweater from the coat closet. "Okay, let's go. I can't wait all day for you."

He shakes his head, accustomed to my sorry attempts at humor. He follows me as I rush out the front door.

"It's beautiful out," I say. The weather is unseasonably warm. Almost sixty degrees. The clean air smells like spring, despite the Christmas decorations that adorn our street and the windows of our neighbors' homes.

We march toward our car. Domenic takes the front passenger seat, sliding the cake boxes from the seat and placing them on his lap.

I press the keys into the ignition, but before starting the car, I say, "Let's pray." I exhale, bowing my head as I notice Domenic do the same from the corner of my eye. "Lord, thank You for leaving your throne of grace in heaven and coming to this earth to walk with us. Thank You for loving us enough to die on that cross. As we remember Your birth this Christmas day and every day, I pray that we would recognize the great sacrifice You made. Help us to live for You and serve You with all our heart and soul and strength. Let us honor You today, Lord. Amen."

Domenic utters a quick prayer, thanking the Lord for his family and for the miracle of Christmas. I can't help but smile. What a difference a year has made.

Since my New Year revelation almost one year ago, so much has changed. With Christ as the head of our home and our lives, our former priorities have shifted. Domenic and I now have daily devotions. We have a scheduled prayer time during which we pray individually and also together. We even have a prayer board where we post requests by category: physical needs, spiritual needs, the unsaved. We sing together. We attend church regularly—and not just on Sunday mornings; midweek services too. We're reading through the Bible. Memorizing Scripture. Domenic has officially joined our church youth group. I joined a women's Bible study and have become active in various ministries.

In every way, I am a new person. A different woman. A reformed mother. Domenic has told me on numerous occasions that he likes the new mom.

"Really?" I ask. "Even though I'm stricter now?"

"You're not really stricter," he corrects me. "You're just more like Mom and Pop now."

He's right. In many areas I have become like my parents. I never thought it could happen. I hear myself saying things like "Let's just trust in the Lord" and "Live for Jesus, Domenic; that's all that matters in this life." When I hear myself say Dad's exact words, as if I've stolen them right out of his mouth, part of me cringes, wondering how I could have evolved into the very thing I despised my whole life. The other half realizes how true it is: that nothing else really matters in this life but living for Christ. All else will pass away.

Mom stands amazed when she hears me tell Domenic things like "I don't want to make a decision without praying about it first" or "Domenic, do you think the Lord would be pleased with your behavior right now?" I can almost read her mind when she stands beside me on those occasions, a quirky grin on her face, listening to my newfound method of discipline: biblically motivated—the same way I was raised.

"Just one of many answered prayers," she tells me, nodding her head in satisfaction.

She thinks it's hilarious when I call their house, on a weekend when Domenic is there, and ask what he's doing, what he's watching, what game he's playing. "He's fine," Mom tells me. "What are you so worried about?"

"I don't want him watching any junk on television," I scold.

"Would I let him watch anything bad?" she snaps back. "You forget I raised two kids of my own."

"You don't know how bad it is out there, Mom," I tell her. I hear her chuckling through the phone. "I'm serious. It's a lot worse now than when I was growing up. I don't want him exposed to the poison that's out there."

They even ask me if he's allowed to watch certain PG-rated movies. "I'm not sure," I say. "I'll have to watch it first and see if it's appropriate."

I'm sure they sometimes wonder, *Who is this new Stephanie? Where did she come from? How did she get this way?* But they don't have to ask; they know what's happened to me. The same thing that happened to them many years ago. Once I was blind, but now I see.

Domenic and I ride with the windows cracked, just to tease our insides with a taste of spring-like air. The ride is clear of any holiday traffic and we cruise across the highway in record time.

I pull into the driveway behind my aunt and uncle's SUV at twenty minutes after one. Knowing my ever-punctual father, who lives by a strict schedule—particularly when food is involved—he's pacing the kitchen in anxious anticipation of our arrival.

We get to the door and I can smell the aroma of garlic and marinara sauce. No need to ring the doorbell or knock. Just as expected, I see Dad's head peek through the curtains as if he's been waiting there forever. He opens the door with a broad smile and his arms spread for a hug.

"Merry Christmas!" he exclaims. Domenic embraces him. Dad grunts with joy, playfully twisting his fist into Domenic's stomach. "I'm gonna lump this kid up, Steph," he says, laughing. "He's getting too big." It's another one of Dad's famous lines, one that we've heard at least a hundred times.

Domenic and I lock eyes and smile. On the ride over, we predicted this exact scene: Dad's embrace, the playful twisting of the fist, the *lumping up* threat. I'm convinced that Dad can't help himself. He loves us all with a pure, unconditional love that doesn't change—just like those quirky one-liners of his.

As we enter the house, Uncle Robert and Aunt Jo Ann greet us with hugs and "Merry Christmases." Their three children—a teenage girl and two younger boys—give us hugs too. Domenic exchanges silly comments with the boys as we make our way through the foyer and into the kitchen.

Finally I see Mom, with her apron on, sauce smeared along her waistline. "Where have you been?" she asks jokingly, pulling Domenic over for a hug. "We're hungry!"

"It's that grandson of yours," I tell her. "He makes me late all the time."

"Don't believe her," Domenic mumbles to Mom.

"I know." She winks at him.

No doubt anxious to eat, Dad claps to draw our attention, "All right, let's gather for prayer and bless the food."

"Aren't we waiting for Michael?" I ask.

"He won't be here until later," Dad says. "I told him we'd start without him." There are few things that keep Dad waiting for his Christmas meal. My notoriously late brother is not one of them.

We assemble around the dining room table, each standing behind his or her assigned seat—perfectly labeled by Mom on stenciled tent cards—and join hands. Dad asks Uncle Robert to lead us all in a Christmas prayer.

I stand beside Domenic, who, at fourteen, is taller than I am and looks so grown up it's scary. The expressions of bewilderment we get from people when we explain that we're mother and son are hysterical. "How old are you?" they ask me. "You don't look old enough to have a teenager."

"I'm not," I reply.

People regularly mistake me for Domenic's big sister or babysitter. I once had to convince a teacher at his school, while attending a back-to-school night, that I was a parent and not a student.

I squeeze Domenic's hand as Uncle Robert thanks the Lord for a holiday that commemorates the birth of our Savior. My son nudges my arm in response, a nonverbal warning that I'd better behave. *It's like Dad with devotions all over again.* But it's different now. I couldn't be more pleased with my son's reaction. He's reverencing His Savior.

After Uncle Robert ends the prayer and we all join him for an *amen*, Dad instructs us to sit. Mom doesn't sit; she immediately heads to the kitchen.

"Angela, wait." Dad grabs her hand. "Before we serve the food, I'd like to take a few minutes for testimonies."

Mom sits, obviously delighted with the opportunity.

Dad starts with a testimony of his own. "It's always a joy to celebrate Christmas with family. And as I look around this table and see what the Lord has done in our lives and how He's brought us together—not only by relation but also in Him—I can't help but give thanks."

The next two testimonies are brief. One sentence each voiced by two of Aunt Jo Ann and Uncle Robert's three children. Uncle Robert then testifies of the Lord's grace and how it defies our comprehension, that the King of Glory would leave His throne, His kingdom, and come to earth and walk among us. "Truly, the Father has lavished His love upon us that He would give His only son—just so that we could be called children of God."[lii,liii]

My heart brims with joy. I can't wait to give thanks for a remarkable year of recovery and restoration. "I have to go next," I announce, not sure if Uncle Robert is finished or not. He tilts his head toward me—nonverbal permission that I can begin.

I take a deep breath, exhaling the elation that wells inside me, then smile broadly. "When I think of where I was this time last year and how differently I led my life, I'm so happy to have been delivered—*from myself.* And I'm thrilled to be able to say that I share in your love for Jesus."

I make eye contact with Uncle Robert and Aunt Jo Ann, then with Mom and Dad. Finally, I turn to Domenic. His face beams proudly back at me. "So many Christmases I've sat in this seat and listened to the rest of you testify about the Lord that I wasn't interested in knowing." My face crinkles at the thought. I shift my eyes to the lighted ceiling, avoiding tears. "I just praise God that He's the God of a second chance."

I pause, realizing there's so much to say but few words with which to describe the unspeakable joy the Father has given me. The joy of being forgiven. My eyes move around the table. "I think that's it."

"Thanks, Steph," Dad says, reaching over the empty chair between us and patting my hand. "We love you, honey."

His eyes reveal a carnal hunger that only Mom's lasagna could fill. "Anyone else before we serve the food?" He waits only a few seconds, searching each person's reaction for a possible taker. Dad wishes everyone a blessed Christmas and stands, motioning for Mom to follow him to the kitchen. She remains seated, her eyes focused on the table centerpiece of red and white carnations.

"I thank God," she says, "that my daughter's here." The tone of her voice and the seriousness of her gaze prompt Dad to retake his seat. "I'm so happy she's here with her son, my grandson." She looks up momentarily and exchanges a smile with Domenic. Her eyes fill with tears. "I'm grateful that they're both serving the Lord." She pauses. "I prayed that someday we'd all sit around this table as a family and talk about Jesus. I never stopped praying or believing." She looks at me. "Even at the height of your rebellion." Looking away, she continues, "It's amazing how the Lord can turn things around. I always knew that He could change our sorrow into joy, and He has." She dabs a napkin under both eyes. "I couldn't ask for a better Christmas present."

As I watch Mom compose herself, I think of the many times she prayed with and for me, the countless occasions on which she assured me that I would return to the Lord. "You will come back to Jesus," she said. And she never doubted.

"Thank you for praying," I say to her and then to Dad.

After a quiet moment at the table of sniffling and grinning, Mom quietly moves from her seat and then into the kitchen. Dad follows. I look at Domenic, who leans his head on my shoulder and smiles. His soft eyes and caring smile are as innocent as they were when he was a child. At fourteen, still only at the onset of those teenage years—which others have warned me about—he's still the same Domenic who followed me around the house as a toddler, vying for my attention. Except now he's an honor student and a killer athlete. And just as Mom and Dad prayed for Michael and me, I pray for my son. I pray that the Lord will preserve Domenic's mind, body, and soul. And so far, He has proven faithful.

What a precious gift the Father has given me, I think, contemplating how marvelously the Lord turned things around in my life. It took me a long time to recognize the miracle God had performed. Long before I ever gave my heart back to Him, the Lord was forming and shaping a tangible demonstration of His restoration and love right in front of me. Even above and beyond my salvation, He freely gave the great gift of love to a wretched, ungrateful sinner like me. He turned my sin, my shame and disgrace—an unwed pregnancy at sixteen—into something beautiful, a treasure. My son. Indeed, that which the enemy meant for evil God turned around for good.[liv]

21 Thank You

Mom and Dad, how can I begin to thank you both for the exemplary lives you led? How can I express my appreciation for the greatest gift any parent could give his or her children: the gift of eternal life, the gift of salvation, the precious gift of Jesus? Nothing I say or do can ever show the depth of gratitude I feel.

I can't thank you both enough for your resolve, your faith and patience with me. Thank you for praying and fasting for me, for undergoing spiritual warfare for my soul.

Thank you for loving Jesus more than anyone or anything else. Thank you for making Him first in everything, the true Center of your lives.

Thank you for taking me to church.

Thank you for hating the things of this world.

Thank you for having devotions with me—even when I begged and pleaded to do other things.

Thank you for sending me to Christian school.

Thank you for not compromising.

Thank you for teaching me that I don't belong to this world, but that my real home is in heaven with Jesus.

Thank you for loving my son as if he were your own. Thank you for raising him while I lived at college.

Thank you for your constant support and love and encouragement.

Thank you again for your prayers.

Above all, thank you for introducing me to a Friend who sticks closer than any brother or sister. Thank you for my Savior. Without Him, I could do nothing. Without Him, my life would have no meaning.

Thank you, Mom and Dad.

Thank you.

Author's Afterward

It's amazing how the Lord works in us personally, how he chases us, whispers to us, loves us.

Like Stephanie, I spent many years apart from Jesus, also taking the long way home. Having had a revelation of my own, however, I've been persuaded that I could never live in separation from my Savior again. He has filled my life with an assurance that I will spend eternity with Him.

Perhaps you are currently taking the "long way home" or have taken the long way home. Perhaps you think that you're too far gone to ever go back. But I assure you that the God of your childhood still loves you and still wants you to be His very own. No matter how far you've strayed or how long you've been away, your heavenly Father is waiting to embrace you, to love you, to welcome you into an eternal reward.

Listen to His calling. Come back to Him.

Perhaps you're a parent and your son or daughter has strayed far from the teachings of his or her childhood. Maybe the very child that you dedicated to Jesus wants nothing to do with Him. I urge you to keep praying, fasting, and believing that God will work a miracle.

Perhaps you've never heard about God's gift of salvation and the content of this book is foreign to you. You may wonder, *How can I be saved?* In this complicated world, God has made salvation simple. "Whoever calls on the name of the Lord shall be saved." (Romans 10:13). Your salvation experience will be the beginning of your relationship with Jesus Christ.

Admit that you're a sinner in need of God. A relationship with Jesus Christ begins with your admission that you need God. You must admit that you need God:
1. To forgive you of your sins, those attitudes or actions that don't meet God's standards. "If we say that we have no sin, we deceive ourselves and the truth is not in us. If we confess our sins, He is faithful and just to forgive us our sins and to cleanse us from all unrighteousness." (1 John 1:8-9)

2. To give you eternal life. "For the wages of sin is death, but the gift of God is eternal life in Christ Jesus our Lord." (Romans 6:23)
3. To show you His purpose for your life. "The thief [Satan] does not come except to steal, and to kill, and to destroy. I [Jesus] have come that they may have life, and that they may have it more abundantly." (John 10:10)

Believe that Jesus died and rose again for your sins. The penalty for your sin is death. But God loves you so much; He provided a way for you to escape that penalty.
1. "For God so loved the world that He gave His only begotten Son, that whoever believes in Him should not perish but have everlasting life." (John 3:16)
2. Jesus can save anyone from an eternity without God. He died and rose again for your justification, to right your relationship with God. "He [Jesus] was delivered over to death for our sins and was raised to life for our justification." (Romans 4:25)
3. Belief in the death and resurrection of Jesus for your sins is essential for salvation, but it is not enough. "You believe that there is one God. You do well. Even the demons believe— and tremble." (James 2:19) You must do more than believe in Jesus. You must confess Him as Lord (boss) of your life.

Confess Jesus as Lord of your life. Confessing Jesus as Lord means to hand over total control of your life to Christ. You give him ownership of your life. He becomes your new boss. If you confess Jesus as Lord of your life, the Bible says you will be saved. "If you confess with your mouth the Lord Jesus and believe in your heart that God has raised him from the dead, you will be saved." (Romans 10:9-10)

I TOOK THE LONG WAY HOME

Acknowledgments

As I wrote this book and recalled and described so many personal experiences, I felt compelled to publicly thank the congregation of First Christian Assembly in Burlington, NJ (1993–1998) for their prayers and unwavering support of my family. You never judged me but instead opened your hearts to me and my son and for that I will always be grateful.

Thank you to Mom and Dad for your unconditional love. Everything written in Chapter 21 is for you.

Thank you to my extended family (too many to name): grandparents (living and deceased), aunts, uncles and cousins. I am convinced that I have been blessed with the most wonderful family in all the world.

Thank you to Sharon Duerr, of First Christian Assembly in Burlington, NJ (1993-1994), who babysat my son Anthony while I was in high school. Thank you for caring for him as your own.

Thank you to my Uncle Ottavio and Aunt Liz for being like my second parents to me, spiritual parents. Your visible growth in Jesus has always motivated me to be a better Christian.

Thank you to Arasi Swamickannu Adkins for being my best friend since fourth grade. You are truly like a sister to me. I consider myself so blessed to have you as a friend.

Thank you to my son Anthony for your love and support and for encouraging me to publish this book when I felt like I shouldn't. Your life has blessed mine so tremendously.

Thank you to Kathy Ide, my amazing editor, for your patience and outstanding editorial guidance.

Thank you to Robert M. Colleluori, my mentor and friend (and quasi-editor), for your inspiration and generosity in helping with the publication of this book. You're the older brother I never had.

References

[i] Vanity of vanities, saith the Preacher, vanity of vanities; all is vanity. (Ecclesiastes 1:2 KJV)

[ii] Francis T. Palgrave, ed (1824–1897). *The Golden Treasury.* 1875.

[iii] Train a child in the way he should go, and when he is old he will not turn from it. (Proverbs 22:6 NIV)

[iv] Luke 15:11-31 NIV.

[v] Whoever trusts in his riches will fall, but the righteous will thrive like a green leaf. (Proverbs 11:28 NIV)

[vi] But seek first his kingdom and his righteousness, and all these things will be given to you as well. (Matthew 6:33 NIV)

[vii] But seek first his kingdom and his righteousness, and all these things will be given to you as well. (Matthew 6:33. NIV)

[viii] What good is it for a man to gain the whole world, yet forfeit his soul? (Mark 8:36 NIV)

[ix] But the LORD said to Samuel, "Do not consider his appearance or his height, for I have rejected him. The LORD does not look at the things man looks at. Man looks at the outward appearance, but the LORD looks at the heart." (1 Samuel 16:7 NIV)

[x] So, because you are lukewarm—neither hot nor cold—I am about to spit you out of my mouth. (Revelation 3:16 NIV)

[xi] Therefore everyone who hears these words of mine and puts them into practice is like a wise man who built his house on the rock. The rain came down, the streams rose, and the winds blew and beat against that house; yet it did not fall, because it had its foundation on the rock. (Matthew 7:23–25 NIV)

[xii] And the peace of God, which transcends all understanding, will guard your hearts and your minds in Christ Jesus. (Philippians 4:7 NIV)

[xiii] Rejoice evermore. Pray without ceasing. In everything give thanks: for this is the will of God in Christ Jesus concerning you. (1 Thessalonians 5:16–18 KJV)

[xiv] But I say unto you, Love your enemies, bless them that curse you, do good to them that hate you, and pray for them which despitefully use you, and persecute you. (Matthew 5:44 KJV)

[xv] But I tell you who hear me: Love your enemies, do good to those who hate you, bless those who curse you, pray for those who mistreat you. (Luke 6:27–28 NIV)

[xvi] A man of many companions may come to ruin, but there is a friend who sticks closer than a brother. (Proverbs 18:24 KJV)

[xvii] I tell you the truth, if you have faith as small as a mustard seed, you can say to this mountain, "Move from here to there," and it will move. Nothing will be impossible for you. (Matthew 17:20, 21 NIV)

[xviii] I can do all things through Christ which strengtheneth me. (Philippians 4:13 KVV)

[xix] The thief cometh not, but for to steal, and to kill, and to destroy: I am come that they might have life, and that they might have it more abundantly. (John 10:10 KJV)

[xx] Jesus said, If you hold to my teaching, you are really my disciples. Then you will know the truth, and the truth will set you free. (John 8:31, 32 NIV)

[xxi] Do not love the world or anything in the world. If anyone loves the world, the Father's love is not in him. For everything that is in the world does not come from the Father. The desires of our flesh and the things our eyes see and want and the pride of this life come from the world. The world and all its desires will pass away. But the man who obeys God and does what He wants done will live forever. (1 John 2:15–17 NIV)

[xxii] But ye are a chosen generation, a royal priesthood, an holy nation, a peculiar people; that ye should show forth the praises of him who hath called you out of darkness into his marvelous light. (1 Peter 2:9 KJV)

[xxiii] And provide for those who grieve in Zion— to bestow on them a crown of beauty instead of ashes, the oil of gladness instead of mourning, and a garment of praise instead of a spirit of despair. They will be called oaks of righteousness, a planting of the LORD for the display of his splendor. (Isaiah 61:3 NIV)

[xxiv] All the believers were together and had everything in common. (Acts 2:44 NIV)

[xxv] Do not store up for yourselves treasures on earth, where moth and rust destroy, and where thieves break in and steal. But store up for yourselves treasures in heaven, where moth and rust do not destroy, and where thieves do not break in and steal. For where your treasure is, there your heart will be also. (Matthew 6:19–21 NIV)

[xxvi] But the LORD said to Samuel, "Do not consider his appearance or his height, for I have rejected him. The LORD does not look at the things man looks at. Man looks at the outward appearance, but the LORD looks at the heart." (1 Samuel 16:7 NIV)

xxvii So, because you are lukewarm—neither hot nor cold—I am about to spit you out of my mouth. (Revelation 3:16 NIV)

xxviii As he was scattering the seed, some fell along the path, and the birds came and ate it up. Some fell on rocky places, where it did not have much soil. It sprang up quickly, because the soil was shallow. But when the sun came up, the plants were scorched, and they withered because they had no root. Other seed fell among thorns, which grew up and choked the plants, so that they did not bear grain. Still other seed fell on good soil. It came up, grew and produced a crop, multiplying thirty, sixty, or even a hundred times. (Mark 4:4–8 NIV)

xxix For I am convinced that neither death nor life, neither angels nor demons, neither the present nor the future, nor any powers, neither height nor depth, nor anything else in all creation, will be able to separate us from the love of God that is in Christ Jesus our Lord. (Romans 8:38–39 NIV)

xxx "I Have Decided to Follow Jesus." Folk song from India. Composer unknown. Public Domain.

xxxi Augustine, E. B. (Edward Bouverie) Pusey, William Benham. *The Confessions of St. Augustine.* 1909.

xxxii Brothers, think of what you were when you were called. Not many of you were wise by human standards; not many were influential; not many were of noble birth. But God chose the foolish things of the world to shame the wise; God chose the weak things of the world to shame the strong. He chose the lowly things of this world and the despised things—and the things that are not—to nullify the things that are. (1 Corinthians 1:26–28 NIV)

xxxiii This righteousness from God comes through faith in Jesus Christ to all who believe. There is no difference, for all have sinned and fall short of the glory of God, and are justified freely by his grace through the redemption that came by Christ Jesus. (Romans 3:22–24 NIV)

xxxiv You did not put oil on my head, but she has poured perfume on my feet. Therefore, I tell you, her many sins have been forgiven—for she loved much. But he who has been forgiven little loves little. (Luke 7:46–48 NIV)

xxxv If you belonged to the world, it would love you as its own. As it is, you do not belong to the world, but I have chosen you out of the world. That is why the world hates you. (John 15:19 NIV) xxxvi No one can serve two masters. Either he will hate the one and love the other, or he will be devoted to the one and despise the other. You cannot serve both God and Money. (Matthew 6:24 NIV)

xxxvii Do not be yoked together with unbelievers. For what do righteousness and wickedness have in common? Or what fellowship can light have with darkness? (2 Corinthians 6:14 NIV)

xxxviii Do you not know that your body is a temple of the Holy Spirit, who is in you, whom you have received from God? You are not your own; you were bought at a price. Therefore honor God with your body. (1 Corinthians 6:19, 20 NIV)

xxxix Only fools refuse to be taught. (Proverbs 1:7–8 The Living Bible)

xl But if serving the LORD seems undesirable to you, then choose for yourselves this day whom you will serve, whether the gods your forefathers served beyond the River, or the gods of the Amorites, in whose land you are living. But as for me and my household, we will serve the LORD. (Joshua 24:15 NIV)

xli Honor your father and mother—which is the first commandment with a promise—that it may go well with you and that you may enjoy long life on the earth. (Ephesians 6:2. NIV)

xlii "For I know the plans I have for you," declares the LORD, "plans to prosper you and not to harm you, plans to give you hope and a future." (Jeremiah 29:11 NIV)

xliii I praise you because I am fearfully and wonderfully made; your works are wonderful, I know that full well. (Psalm 139:14 NIV)

xliv For you created my inmost being; you knit me together in my mother's womb. (Psalm 130:13 NIV)

xlv Are not two sparrows sold for a penny? Yet not one of them will fall to the ground apart from the will of your Father. And even the very hairs of your head are all numbered. So don't be afraid; you are worth more than many sparrows. (Matthew 10:29–31 NIV)

xlvi No one will be able to stand up against you all the days of your life. As I was with Moses, so I will be with you; I will never leave you nor forsake you. (Joshua 1:5 NIV)

xlvii Dear friends, I urge you, as aliens and strangers in the world, to abstain from sinful desires, which war against your soul. 1 Peter 2:11 NIV) xlviii He bestows rain on the earth; he sends water upon the countryside. (Job 5:10 NIV)

xlix You are the light of the world. A city on a hill cannot be hidden. Neither do people light a lamp and put it under a bowl. Instead they put it on its stand, and it gives light to everyone in the house. (Matthew 5:14–15 NIV)

l You sweep men away in the sleep of death; they are like the new grass of the morning—though in the morning it springs up new, by evening it is dry and withered. (Psalm 90:5–6 NIV)

li All men are like grass, and all their glory is like the flowers of the field; the grass withers and the flowers fall, but the word of the Lord stands forever. (1 Peter 1:24–25 NIV)

lii How great is the love the Father has lavished on us, that we should be called children of God! And that is what we are! The reason the world does not know us is that it did not know him. (1 John 3:1 NIV)

liii This is how much God loved the world: He gave his Son, his one and only Son. And this is why: so that no one need be destroyed; by believing in him, anyone can have a whole and lasting life. God didn't go to all the trouble of sending his Son merely to point an accusing finger, telling the world how bad it was. He came to help, to put the world right again. Anyone who trusts in him is acquitted; anyone who refuses to trust him has long since been under the death sentence without knowing it. And why? Because of that person's failure to believe in the one-of-a-kind Son of God when introduced to him. (John 3:16–18 The Message)

liv As for you, you meant evil against me, but God meant it for good in order to bring about this present result, to preserve many people alive. (Genesis 50:20 NASB)